Praise for *Eating Less*

"Gillian Riley's approach [...] its effect on people's lives."

Leslie Kenton, health expert and writer

"Immensely interesting and helpful. Empowers those who previously have felt themselves to be the victims of dieting and dietary advice."

Dorothy Rowe, psychologist and writer

"Excellent marriage guidance counselling for those with a difficult relationship with food."

Patrick Holford, author and founder, Institute For Optimum Nutrition

"This book will be invaluable not only to people with an overeating problem but to those who are counselling them as well."

Joe Griffin, psychotherapist and writer

"One woman I worked with recently had undergone therapy at a NHS funded clinic and she said your book gave her more insight in the few days she took to read it than months of counselling."

Maggie Preston, MA, counsellor

"I like the simplicity of the EATING LESS system; the basic principles are amazingly easy to understand and follow. Most importantly, I've lost many of my fears around the topic of food – fear of going out of control, fear of failure – and this gives me confidence that this is the permanent solution to my problem. I've found that I really can trust myself around food – even regaining my sense of humour about it all!"

Mirjam Bollag Dondi, psychotherapist, Institute of Applied Psychology, Zurich

Praise for *Eating Less* by Gillian Riley from readers

"As a fifty-year-old woman who has dieted since the age of fifteen, I wanted to tell you of my response to reading EATING LESS. As I worked through, chapter by chapter, it took me on a painful journey of self-examination and facing truths I had denied all those years. Gradually, a huge sense of release and relief took over. Your book showed me the way to confront and address my addiction to food. It gave me simple tools to examine my behaviour and begin to take control of the only area of my life I wanted to radically change. It was like stepping off a treadmill, calling halt to a behavioural pattern which led to misery and failure. A huge weight(!) has been lifted and the food which I love is no longer the source of terror it was before.

Your book is entirely new in its approach and answered every question almost before I'd asked it."

Sarah Kaye, teacher, Wiltshire

"Your book is the answer to a prayer. You have blown away all the myths surrounding dieting, weight loss and body size, and you have called a spade a spade. I needed this kind of straight talk. Although I had known for many years I was actually addicted to food, I didn't know what to do about it."

Cheryl Joyce, county council employee, Cambridgeshire

"I can only say I am astonished at my change of attitude to food, eating, my body, my health and my weight. I really did feel your book and your technique was my last chance at finding a way out of the mental muddle I had got myself into, over eating and weight. I wasn't sure it would make a difference and at first I couldn't put it into practice. Then the penny dropped and I am delighted to tell you that I haven't looked back since.

I now make healthy choices, think carefully about quantity, and best of all, don't feel any kind of deprivation at all. I feel strong, liberated and intelligent about it. I have of course lost weight! I still occasionally weigh myself, but not in an obsessive way, and I have never lost weight before in such a detached manner, if you know what I mean."

Maggi Hooper, housewife and mother, Surrey

EATING
LESS

take control
of overeating

Gillian Riley

Vermilion
LONDON

First published in Great Britain in 1998

5 7 9 10 8 6

Text © Gillian Riley 1998, 1999
Illustrations © Random House Group Ltd 1999

Gillian Riley has asserted her right to be identified as the author of this work under the Copyright, Designs and Patents Act 1988.

First published in the United Kingdom in 1998 by Gillian Riley
This new edition published in the United Kingdom in 1999 by Vermilion
an imprint of Ebury Press
Random House, 20 Vauxhall Bridge Road, London SW1V 2SA

Random House Australia (Pty) Limited
20 Alfred Street, Milsons Point, Sydney, New South Wales 2061, Australia

Random House New Zealand Limited
18 Poland Road, Glenfield, Auckland 10, New Zealand

Random House South Africa (Pty) Limited
Endulini, 5A Jubilee Road, Parktown 2193, South Africa

The Random House Group Limited Reg. No. 954009

www.randomhouse.co.uk

A CIP catalogue record for this book is available from the British Library.

ISBN 0 09 182615 2

Papers used by Vermilion are natural, recyclable products made from wood grown in sustainable forests.

Typeset by Digital Type, London
Printed and bound by Cox & Wyman, Reading, Berks

Contents

'God gave me luck, health,
a voice and certain intelligence.
But if I could live my life over again,
there is one thing I would change.
I would want to be able to eat less.'

Luciano Pavarotti
(reported in *Time* magazine,
December 1997)

1 A New Look

As you are no doubt aware, there is no shortage of books, magazine articles and TV programmes on the subjects of eating and weight loss. I'm fascinated by all of it and always look to see if anybody else is working along the same lines as I am. The more I investigate, the more I see how different my approach really is.

Each of these approaches makes its own unique contribution, but many contain similar themes, so I want to let you know right from the start that I'm not going to be repeating them. This is not to say that these ideas aren't valuable in many ways, it's just that they don't answer all of my questions. Perhaps they don't answer all of yours either.

Here are most of the main themes, and some of my thoughts about them:

☐ **Excess weight is not a health problem, so it's best to learn to love your body exactly as it is and accept yourself as a beautiful, heavier person.**
I think it's a very good idea to love your body, but it's equally important to be honest about the fact that overeating does affect your health.

An Expert Panel on Healthy Weight, appointed by the American Health Foundation in 1996, studied the research and concluded that for the best possible health, body mass index should be between 19 and 25. (Body mass index, or BMI, takes your height into account as well as your weight – see Reference 1 to calculate yours.) Risks for heart disease, high blood pressure, diabetes and many other diseases start to rise significantly with a BMI of 25 and above. (1)

Eating Less will show you how to make changes, not encourage you to settle for the way things are.

☐ **Overeating is the result of not dealing with your emotions. Learn to respond constructively to your true feelings, and you will no longer need to overeat.**
If this is true, then why do people overeat when they're content, perhaps at a delightful dinner party? And why do people overeat even though they have become very skilled at dealing with their emotions – those who have been in therapy and therapists themselves, for example?

I know several people who overeat who also deal with their emotions in positive and powerful ways. And I know people who are emotionally not at all on top of things, who do not overeat, or take drugs, drink or smoke. Perhaps you can think of people like this too.

It's true there is often a connection between negative emotional states and addictive behaviour of any kind, but this isn't the whole story.

☐ **Dieting makes you fat. Stop dieting and let your body find its natural weight.**
We all know diets don't last, and, as we'll discuss later, dieting usually makes eating problems even worse in the long term. But what can you do instead? What you need is a way to control your overeating that is sustainable in the long term. Otherwise, even if you find your natural weight, you won't be able to maintain it. This book will show you how.

☐ **Eat only when you are genuinely hungry.**
The main problem with this is that most people, especially those who overeat, find it extremely difficult to correctly identify genuine hunger. As an obese client said recently: 'I don't think I'd recognise natural hunger if it jumped up and bit me on the nose.'

Many people seem to feel hungry *after* eating a meal. In fact, it's quite possible you could conjure up some feelings of hunger almost any time at all. On the other hand, it is possible to go without eating for very long periods of time and still not feel any physical sensation of hunger. I experience this myself at times. I do not feel hungry, even though this makes no sense considering when and how much I last ate.

Another problem with making hunger your cue to eat is simply that it can often be very inconvenient. If you are eating with others, in a restaurant for example, it seems silly to suggest that you delay your meal until you are sure your hunger has appeared. And it may not be practical to skip a meal at lunchtime because you're not hungry, only to find you are hungry an hour or two later – during a shift at work, in a meeting or when you need to pick up the kids from school.

It makes sense to aim for hunger as a sign to eat, but you will also need a guideline that's more tangible and is therefore less easily misinterpreted – and something that fits your own schedule!

☐ **Stop eating when you are full.**
It's even more difficult to be sure you've reached the right amount of fullness. Most people don't feel the 'fullness' of what they ate until quite a few minutes after finishing a meal. If you tend to overeat, this is too late. (2)

Unfortunately, genuine body signals are often subtle and hard to read. Even when you are aware of them, you can very easily override them.

☐ **Addictive cravings are the result of biochemical imbalances or nutritional deficiencies.**
A common example of this theory is the idea that a craving for chocolate indicates the body's need for magnesium. The notion that our bodies give us signals telling us what we need to eat is very common, but, as we will see later, this is far from a complete explanation for addictive eating.

Here's a question to ponder: if I'm wanting to eat chocolate because my body needs magnesium, why don't I also crave green leafy vegetables such as kale, which contain even more of this mineral?

☐ **Abstinence from all 'binge' or 'trigger' foods must be - maintained.**
According to one book that promotes this idea, abstinence must include all forms of flour, sugar, chocolate, nuts, bananas,

honey, bread, dried fruits, alcohol and caffeine, to name but a few from the list of fifty categories of addictive food.

I think it's true for most people that certain foods are more difficult to eat in a controlled way than others. But in the long term, abstinence from so many foods is burdensome, unrealistic and, most importantly, not at all necessary. A strategy for taking control will be more effective if it's attractive to you, if it's something you really do want to live with. And it needs to be flexible enough to suit you and your unique requirements and preferences, so that it's something you can live with.

□ **Overeating is a rebellion against our culture's unrealistic expectations of what women should be and look like.**
Cultural stereotypes of women and the pressure they create can at best only partly explain overeating. If we compare the current figures for obesity in men and women in Britain, one in eight men and one in six women are considered to be obese (roughly 20 kilos/3 stone overweight). Yes, there is a difference between the sexes, but not a lot, and at least part of the difference could be due to the tendency of women's bodies to store fat more easily.

It's true we are bombarded with images of skinny women but those images do not control your behaviour. *You* do. The fact is that there are women who have managed to make lasting changes in their eating patterns, but the culture didn't change. *They* did. One thing addicts tend to do is find something or someone else to blame for their problems, and often the easiest things to blame are those that are the most remote and intangible. The liberating truth is you can take control of your eating in any cultural setting.

Mind Control

So how can it be that I have something different to say on this well-worn topic? It's simply because I approach the subject of overeating from a different perspective. That perspective is one of psychological addiction: the aspect of addiction that exists in the way we think.

I have been teaching people about addiction since 1982. I have mainly focused on helping people to stop smoking, and achieve extremely high rates of success by explaining to smokers what psychological addiction is and how to deal with it. When this is understood, smokers are able not only to stop smoking, but stay stopped in the long term.

This is a crucial point, because many smokers find they can stop, but return to smoking later on because they haven't dealt with the psychological side of their addiction. In other words, they haven't changed the way they think about smoking.

In the same way, many overeaters are able to diet temporarily, but return to overeating because they haven't changed the way they think about eating.

Not only do my clients stop smoking, but many of them are pleasantly surprised to find they can do so without gaining any weight. This is because when they deal correctly with one addiction (smoking), they don't need to replace it with another (eating).

There is also a certain kind of smoker for whom smoking isn't really much of a problem at all. They are not really smokers. They are overeaters, and the only reason they ever smoke is because they don't know how else to control their addictive eating. The smoking part of stopping smoking is relatively easy for them. Their challenge is in facing up to their eating addiction.

Apart from smokers, I also work with people who want to make changes in their eating. These clients tell me it is extremely helpful to them to call overeating an addiction. When they start to handle their problem as an addiction, they begin to see things about their overeating that they had previously not seen, and as a result develop a degree of control they previously didn't have.

Finally, a confession. I eat – and I certainly have the ability to overeat. As a result, every word I write on this subject has been tested by my personal experience. This approach is all I'll ever use or need.

I strongly suspect I have as happy a relationship with food as anyone you'll ever meet. My weight fluctuates very little and I am in no sense at war with myself, either with my shape or what I eat. I am keenly aware of my addictive thinking, and I believe it is nothing but this awareness that gives me the ability to be in control of my eating.

This is a book about taking control of addictive overeating. It is not a book about nutrition; there are already many excellent books available on the subject. Neither is it a book for people who are anorexic or bulimic, or for those addicted to exercise, although it's possible they could benefit from reading it.

It is for people who are overweight. Either a bit overweight or a lot overweight, or those who can't seem to get out of that cycle of dieting and regaining weight over and over again.

This book is for people who have the same sorts of problems with food that other people have with cigarettes or other drugs.

If you've ever thought to yourself that you are addicted to food, this book is for you.

In other words   **DIANE**

For the past fifteen years I had been struggling with what I eat, how I eat and what I weigh. I have tried numerous approaches: nutritionists, self-help groups, specific diets. Although some of these have helped, the sense of struggle I felt around eating remained.

I was drawn to reading Eating Less *and participating in the course because I knew about the success Gillian has had with helping people give up smoking. For me, eating is another addiction like smoking.* Eating Less *offers something unique and groundbreaking.*

For the first time in my life I feel a sense of freedom around what I eat. I can apply a set of useful techniques, and my obsession with food is diminishing. Eating has become a natural process that I do at mealtimes without being fearful of how much I will eat, or wondering if I will be able to stop. The freedom I feel is such an enormous gift. My self-esteem has risen, I feel more in control of my life and more confident.

TAKING CONTROL

• At the end of each chapter you'll find a section like this one. It highlights specific points raised in the chapter, and suggests mental and written exercises, and changes for you to bring into your life. These exercises and suggestions will enable you to integrate this approach into your life so that you can make the changes you want to in your behaviour.

• You may want to read this book on your own, or create a group to meet and discuss it on a regular basis. Or you may want to find a counsellor or therapist with whom you can explore the themes I describe. All of these are possibilities for you to choose from, depending on your own needs and circumstances. It's impossible to be too specific, because each of us will have varying degrees of difficulty with these subjects.

• My main advice at the start, as I advise each of my clients, is that you don't make this technique the subject of general discussion with family and friends. Your relationship with the food you eat is personal, private and unique; making a change in that relationship needs to be personal and private too. The people in your life may eat with you and even cook for you, but finally it's up to you and you alone what goes in your mouth.

You might be tempted to explain what you've learned in this book in order to help others with their eating problems. I strongly advise you against this as it is likely to be met with resistance and could impair your own progress. By all means let them know about this book, but then leave them alone to decide whether or not they want to read and use it.

This suggestion to keep it private may seem unusual. If you often talk with friends about food and weight issues this advice may seem difficult to follow, and at this stage in the book you may not see the point of it. However, it makes this technique much easier to use, and as you read on you will see why. I'm mentioning it at the beginning so that you can keep a low profile on what you're doing right from the start.

References

1. These recommendations are reported in the *American Journal of Clinical Nutrition* (1996; 63, 474S-7S). A great number of studies substantiate them; one of the most significant is the Nurses Health Study, conducted by Harvard University researchers and published in *The New England Journal of Medicine* (1995; 333, 677–685). This study followed 115,195 women over 16 years and concludes:
    'Body weight and mortality from all causes were directly related among these middle-aged women. Lean women did not have excess mortality.'
    To find your body mass index (BMI), divide your weight in kilos by the square of your height in metres. For example, let's say your height is 1.6 metres. The square of that (1.6 x 1.6) is 2.56. Let's say your weight is 67.6 kilos. 67.6 divided by 2.56 is 26, so 26 is your BMI. A BMI of 25 and over is considered overweight and 30 obese.
2. Dr Andrew Prentice, Director of the Medical Research Council Dunn Clinical Nutrition Centre, writes:
    'Physiological studies show that human metabolism is very poorly adapted to recognise excess fat consumption.'
    British Medical Bulletin 1997; 53, 229–237.

2 Control Your Eating, Not Your Weight

People *can* change. *Everybody* can. In fact, all of us do change, simply because things happen to us as we go through our lives that inevitably make an impact and leave us different in some way. The question is not whether we change, but how much we passively drift into it and how much we direct change, actively choosing to create the person we really want to be.

There are two crucial things to know about directing this kind of change. It never happens overnight, and it never gets done for you. Change takes time and it takes effort on your part. Right now, for example, you can't help but use your time and effort in order to read this.

However, when it comes to your weight – your body size and shape – it may well be that you've already spent considerable time and effort on making changes, but you've found the changes you tried to make either didn't work or didn't last. This, of course, can leave you doubting your ability to make the changes you want.

If what you tried before was some form of diet, then at least know you're not alone: according to many surveys, as many as 95 per cent of people who diet regain all the weight they lose. Maybe that's why you're reading this book. You are looking for something else.

Welcome to a completely different solution. This is not a diet book. This book is about making real, lasting change. The ideas I'll be introducing may not be easy to take on board and use immediately. This doesn't mean they aren't sound or that you are incapable of using them. It just means this will take time.

After all, it took you this long in your life to get to where you are now, so isn't it reasonable to take some time and effort to make effective changes? You may want an easy, instant cure, but is that really possible? What I hope to show you in these pages is that quick-fix solutions – diets, pills, magic slimming techniques – at best avoid the real problem, and can actually make it worse.

Your Problem Isn't Weight

In fact, you may not even be seeing what the real problem is in the first place. The chances are, you think your problem – what you want to *change* – is your weight. Ask yourself this: if your body size and shape were how you wanted and they stayed that way, would you be reading this book? If you answer: 'Of course not!' then here's something for you to think about.

Imagine a smoker who says: 'I'm coughing too much, what can I do to stop my coughing?' Someone points out that it's the smoking that's doing it, but the smoker says: 'Yes, I know, but all I really want is some good cough medicine.' Imagine a drinker who says: 'My driving is terrible – I keep having accidents. Where can I get some good driving lessons?' Someone suggests it's because he's driving drunk, so he keeps drinking and takes the bus.

Now, you may know that smokers and drinkers go through periods of time when they do think like this. It's called denial, because they are denying the reality of what their problem actually is. The difference is that when they finally admit they do have a problem, they tend to see it for what it is. Smokers set out to take control of their smoking, not their coughing. And drinkers set out to take control of their drinking, not their driving.

When it comes to eating, though, this step is often not taken, or not taken fully. People who overeat set out to take control of a symptom: their weight. They keep their sights set on the effect – not the cause, which is overeating.

The typical overeater says: 'I'm two stone overweight, none of my clothes fit properly and I hate how I look. How can I lose weight?' So if someone says: 'What you need to do is eat less food,' they reply: 'I know. I'll join a slimming group.'

You see, your weight is not your problem. It's one of the effects of your problem. Your problem is you eat more food than your body needs. Not more than somebody else's body needs. More than your body needs. Not more than your body used to need when you were younger or more active. More than your body needs now. Not more than your body would need if you had different genes and metabolism. More than your body needs with the genes and metabolism you have. That's why there's extra weight on it.

Saying the problem is 'eating' and not 'weight' might sound at first like I'm just playing with words, but let's think about it because it's very important. *The reason it's important is because the more attached you are to losing weight, the more difficult it will be for you to stay in control of your overeating.* (1)

Let's start to look at why.

The Problems with Having Weight Loss as your Main Goal

☐ **Yo-yo dieting**   When weight loss is all you care about, it makes sense to follow a diet. But whenever you go on a diet, it's inevitable that you'll abandon it sooner or later. A diet may help you to lose weight, but it's only a temporary solution to a permanent problem: your potential for overeating.

When weight is all you care about, your motivation disappears along with the weight. So it's only when weight has gone back on that you start to think about taking some action. Then you are in that familiar – and unhealthy – cycle of weight loss and gain and loss and gain, known as yo-yo dieting or weight cycling.

☐ **Poor nutrition**   When weight loss is all you care about, it's easier to ignore the nutritional value of the food you eat. You may not be giving your body the nutrition it needs, even eating things which do more harm than good, but when weight loss is your priority that's what influences your decisions. You could end up doing things like passing on the beans and rice at dinner because they're 'fattening' but snacking on biscuits later that evening because you fancy them (. . . and after all, you've been so good all day, you skipped lunch and you're going to the gym tomorrow so you'll work off the extra calories).

☐ **An unhappy relationship with food**   When weight loss is all you care about, you can end up feeling guilty about eating anything because all food contains calories. Especially after years of calorie-counting, your choices about what to eat can become harder to make because any choice to eat feels like a bad one.

☐ **An unhealthy effect on your body**   When weight loss is all you care about, your results can be elusive and misleading. Weight loss is often *muscle* loss, which is not only damaging to your health but means excess fat can become even more of a problem later on.

On the other hand, if you eat wisely and take even moderate exercise, the lean muscle you gain can outweigh much of the fat you've lost. This means your weight doesn't change as much as your health and appearance does.

As an example, one woman who took part in a two-month study of a nutritional product lost less than half a kilo (a mere 1 lb) but dropped three dress sizes. She had lost 4 kilos (9 lb) of fat and at the same time gained 3.5 kilos (8lb) of muscle. She looked quite different of course, and, most importantly, this change in body composition made her considerably more healthy. (2)

☐ **Avoiding the real problem**   When weight loss is all you care about, you avoid facing the reality of your addiction to food. After all, you're not addicted to weight: you don't get cravings late at night for a kilo of fat to add to your thighs.

When weight loss is all you care about, it makes sense to avoid your compulsive desire to overeat. For example, if you tend to overeat late at night, you keep yourself busy in the evenings and avoid being alone at home. This has to be a temporary measure, and when the food addict in you resurfaces, the weight goes right back on, because dealing with your addictive eating was never your goal. Weight loss was.

☐ **Poor motivation**   When weight loss is all you care about, it's more difficult to stay motivated because there will always be the days when, for various reasons, you just feel 'fat' no matter what you've been eating. Whether this perception is real or imagined, it can make any sense of success very short-lived.

When weight loss is your goal you never really achieve it, partly because it's never enough (remember the saying: 'You can never be too rich or too thin'?) and partly because you fear you won't stay that way. It's such a fragile achievement.

Most important of all, weight loss as a goal makes it easy to disregard the damage overeating does to your health, your vitality and your self-esteem – in ways that have nothing to do with how you look. We'll look at this in more detail later.

Why the Problem Can Be So Hard to See

Have you heard the story about someone asking a fish what water is like, and the fish answers: 'What's water?' In much the same way, we are swimming around in a culture obsessed with appearance, and we are so used to it that we simply don't see how much it surrounds us. Just like the fish that takes water for granted, we accept the wrong message – that appearance is all that matters – without question.

This attitude is so common, it's everywhere. For example, when I first started writing this book I told many people I met that I was writing a book about addictive eating. Every one of them who mentioned it later referred to it as a book about losing weight. I even have a friend who calls it 'your fat book'! And yet people would never call my book on stopping smoking a book about improving lung capacity.

Let's take this slowly, because this is a very tricky point. It might seem simple, but there can be a huge gulf between understanding it and embracing it fully.

For example, you may well be thinking that you really do want to deal with your eating problem. But ask yourself if it's still only a means to an end. Ask yourself how much your priority has to do with your appearance, if you only want to control your overeating in order to be a certain size and shape.

Here's another example. A woman phoned me up last week to enquire about coming to see me for help. She sounded very distressed, quite out of control of her eating and frantic about her weight. She wasn't sure whether to see me or join a Weight Watchers group much nearer to her home. 'I have a friend who has just lost 28 lb with Weight Watchers!' she cried down the phone. 'She's a very old friend!' She was extremely agitated about it and it was obvious that what had distressed her so much was her friend's weight loss. It's impossible to imagine her saying, with that same tone of fury in her voice: 'My friend has been eating a lot less food!' And yet this must be what the friend had done.

My irate caller, like so many others, is obsessed with the effect instead of the cause.

Taking Control of Overeating

Some people, of course, do give up their goal of losing weight – but they don't replace it with any other eating-related goals. They just give up doing anything about any of it. You may identify with this, or fear it is what will happen if you let go of your attachment to weight loss as your principal goal.

The solution is to understand how else you will benefit from taking control of your overeating. One benefit will be weight loss, and, provided you are in fact overweight, there is nothing wrong with that at all. However, in order to do this, you need to make your body size less important to you and make taking control of your overeating your main goal. This requires a change in your thinking, a shifting of priorities.

Taking control of our eating enables us to get to grips with addiction. However, at first glance the word 'control' might imply anorexia to you. You might fear you could end up having so much control over your eating that you hardly ate at all. On the contrary, eating too little is just as much a result of being out of control as eating too much. Those with anorexia fear addictive eating so much that they seek safety in eating almost nothing. After all, abstinence is usually recommended for most addictions. Unfortunately, though, unlike other addictions, abstinence doesn't work so well with food! I use the phrase 'taking control of your eating' to include taking the best care of your health that you can. (3)

As we will see later on, there are many different things that act together to create an eating problem. *One of the most significant is deciding to make your appearance more important to you than your health.* To look good, at any cost. To believe that what matters is having the 'perfect' figure, and that what matters less, if at all, is becoming malnourished through your efforts to achieve it. Anorexia and bulimia are extreme results of this, but it's relevant to us all to varying degrees. Extra weight is almost universally judged, scorned and ridiculed, and it is precisely this that encourages us to attach ourselves so strongly and exclusively to the goal of weight loss.

Losing weight is a likely consequence of taking control of overeating. But when we are preoccupied with our appearance, which is a material concern, we pay less attention to the effects of addiction and what it costs us emotionally and spiritually to be out of control in such a significant area of our lives. And in many subtle and insidious ways we take less notice of the cost to our physical health as well.

The point is that while you are overeating, you are holding yourself back from becoming all you could be, in ways that have nothing to do with the size and shape of your body.

Of course, if you are like most addicts, you reason that when you have sorted yourself out and become all you can be (whatever that means to you) then you will be able to control your overeating. This is putting the cart before the horse. The process of taking control of your overeating is a path – perhaps *the* path – towards a more confident, peaceful, happier and more fulfilled you. Making positive eating choices for the right reasons can lead you directly towards becoming the person you want to be and living your life the way you really want to live it.

I'm suggesting you pursue a new goal: taking control of your overeating because that's your main source of physical and psychological well-being. Then losing weight becomes a bonus.

Why It's Vital to Change Priorities

Perhaps by now you are beginning to think: 'Yes, but what does it mean to be in control of my eating and how do I do it?' Great! These are good questions to be asking, and you are in the right place to get the answers: they are what this book is all about. Just understand that they are very different questions from: 'How do I lose weight?' *The first step in learning to control your overeating is to stop asking how you lose weight.*

This might look like too big a change for you to make. If you are completely preoccupied with wanting to change the shape and size of your body, it may seem impossible to start to care more about your eating. But look at it this way: if you are going on a hundred-mile journey due south, and you turn a fraction to the left and take your journey slightly south-east, after a hundred miles you will end up in a very different place. Begin this hundred-mile journey (it's actually a journey that will take you the rest of your life, as you are going to be eating for the rest of your life) by acknowledging that your best goal is to be in control of your eating.

Weight loss as a principal goal is fundamentally flawed. It addresses the effect, not the cause, of your problem, and only one effect at that. It's the one we can all see, but I want to suggest to you it's not even the most important one.

Being in control of your eating has far more significant implications. And wanting to lose weight could be the one thing that keeps you from appreciating what these implications are, because when weight loss is all you care about, you invalidate these other, truly life-enhancing rewards. We will go into this more deeply in the next two chapters.

In other words   TULLIA

I started to have eating problems roughly fifteen years ago. I sought help, but because I was not overweight, anorexic or bulimic, nobody would give me help.

I kept on eating junk food even though I had signs of poor health: unpleasant mood swings, PMS, fluid retention, fatigue, frequent nausea and abdominal bloating. I wanted to change but I thought there was no way out. Besides, most of the time I was denying the problem to myself, very much helped by the fact that it was never a weight problem, so I could conceal it.

Once I came to terms with the reality that I was addicted to food, a whole process of change began. I became engaged in a process of self-discovery that has gone far beyond the tangible consequences of overeating.

At first I had a huge resistance to change, yet the more I practise, the more I feel at ease with it and as a consequence with myself.

TAKING CONTROL

• It takes deliberate and conscious effort to change your goal from wanting to lose weight to wanting to control your overeating. Whenever you think about your weight, think:

> 'Weight is not my problem. Eating is.'

This is true whether you are underweight, a bit overweight or a lot overweight. It could even be true if you are the weight you want to be.

If you tend to be very concerned about your weight, it may not at first seem true to think of your problem as 'eating' rather than 'weight'. This requires a significant change in your thinking. Stay with this, though, because you will find a breakthrough for yourself. Keep reviewing this book and take note of the ways in which changing this emphasis benefits you.

By the way, when I refer to 'weight' I mean it to include the shape and the size of your body. 'Shape', 'size' and 'weight' all refer to the same thing: your appearance. They are different ways of describing one of the effects of your problem, not the cause, which is overeating.

• If you normally weigh yourself, put your bathroom scales away. Unless you have a particular reason for knowing your weight, such as filling in an insurance form or for medical reasons, weigh yourself no more than once or twice a year, if that.

When you weigh yourself over and over again you are using your weight to judge whether you are succeeding or failing. In this book I will show you how to create a different standard of success, one which relates to how much you are in control of your eating. In order to take on this new standard, you will need to let go of your old standard.

• You may react to some things in later chapters by asking yourself: 'But how will that help me to lose weight?' Change the question to: 'How will that help me to take control of my eating?' and you will see the answer.

References

1. 'The more unhappy you are with your figure the less likely you are to lose weight. Scientists found that those who are most dissatisfied with their bodies have the most trouble sticking to diet and fitness programmes.'
    The *Daily Mail*, September 2, 1998, reporting on a study conducted at Stanford University School of Medicine

2   'Your problem is not excess weight so much as it is excess body fat coupled with too little muscle . . . it's imperative that you look beyond the simplistic notion of losing weight and concentrate on building muscle at the expense of fat.'
    From *Biomarkers: The Ten Keys to Prolong Vitality*, by Drs William

Evans and Irwin Rosenberg of Tufts University Department of Nutrition and Medicine, USA (Simon & Schuster).

Muscle weighs considerably more than fat, so a body-builder, for example, will weigh more but carry less fat than their BMI would suggest.

The nutritional product being studied was *Juice Plus*. See Reference 4 for Chapter 12.

3. *The Anorexia Nervosa Reference Book* by Roger Slade includes the following as part of a definition of the condition:
    'Steadfast and overriding, though often denied, preoccupation with first pursuing a low body weight and then maintaining it . . .' and 'To safeguard herself against what [she] calls "losing control" – meaning not being able to stop eating – she strives to remain abnormally thin.'

3 All That Glitters ...

Every day you make choices about food. You may be in a restaurant choosing from a menu, or in a supermarket choosing what to have for dinner that evening. Or you may be standing in your kitchen, trying to decide on a late night snack before bed. Every day, you choose when to eat, what to eat and how much to eat.

In some way, these choices are a problem for you. You eat things and later regret it. You make promises not to eat certain kinds of foods but find you don't stick to them. You follow a diet for a while but sooner or later find yourself overeating again.

We will look at how to decide when, what and how much to eat in later chapters. First, let's look at another factor involved in making a choice: the reasons why you might choose either to eat or not to eat something.

Motivation ('Why am I doing this?') is crucial: it can make the difference between success and failure in anything you attempt to do. For example, if I asked you to give me twenty pounds, you would most likely want to know why. If I said that in return I'd give you a big smile, you probably wouldn't give me the money. But if I said that in return I'd give you a beautiful diamond ring, it would be more likely to provide you with the motivation. In both cases, the action – giving me twenty pounds – is the same. But without good motivation you may not choose to take the action.

When it comes to your choices about food ('Why am I eating/not eating this?') I want to suggest to you that at the heart of your motivation lies a very basic concept: self-esteem. Simply put, self-esteem is the opinion you have of yourself. It's impossible to have no opinion at all, and even though you may not spend much time thinking about what it is, this opinion does have a profound effect on your daily life. Just as the opinion you have of someone else affects every moment you spend with that person, so the opinion you have of yourself affects you.

A poor opinion means you experience low self-esteem, which can lead to persistent feelings of anxiety, insecurity and guilt, even when there is no good reason for these feelings. Positive opinions mean high self-esteem: confidence and ease with oneself, and an ability to accept mistakes and shortcomings as well as compliments and success.

It's natural to prefer to feel worthy and capable rather than inadequate and inferior, so when we try to make changes in our lives – going on a diet, for example – one of the main reasons we do it is to feel better about ourselves, to respect and honour ourselves a bit more. In other words, we do it in order to raise our self-esteem.

But in trying to feel better about themselves, many people make a fundamental mistake: they try to raise their self-esteem by gaining the approval of other people. We try to prove our worth to others so that we'll feel more worthy inside. And this is not just something we try on every now and then; it can become a significant part of daily life, our main motivation for doing almost anything at all.

Other people's approval of you is not a bad thing – it's just the wrong place to look for self-esteem. Not only is it the wrong place, it can keep self-esteem low. This is because we can end up valuing the approval of others so much that our private achievements become utterly insignificant. Our own approval of ourselves can matter so little that we don't even stop to consider it. Indeed a strong need to please others (or at least avoid their judgement and rejection, which is really the same thing) is usually a sign of low self-esteem. In the absence of genuine esteem, we try any way we can to 'prove' our value to somebody else.

We may try to impress others by owning more things or bigger and better things. Or we may seek approval by working harder, achieving more or by being more caring and helpful. And a great many of us try by making ourselves look better – by which, of course, we mean thinner. *Wanting to own a better body can be just as much an attempt to gain self-esteem as is any other possession or achievement that's designed to impress others.*

I suspect that many people want to lose weight *primarily* in order that other people will approve of them more. This is especially true of women, because that's what our culture promotes and rewards, but I suspect this is true of many men, too.

It is true that most people approve of slimmer bodies rather than fatter ones. The problem is that when improving your appearance is the main – perhaps *only* – motivation behind your eating choices, you will tend to attach less significance to the private source of genuine self-esteem: your own opinion of yourself, regardless of what others may think. *And it's the private sources of genuine self-esteem that provide you with much more effective motivation when it comes to taking control of an addiction.*

The truth is I do like to be admired by others for being slim. But I also know a danger lurks in this way of thinking. It's dangerous because it can take me away from my genuine self-esteem and impair my relationship with food, so it's a kind of motivation I don't deliberately encourage, either in myself or in others.

Whether we consider ourselves to be overweight or not, our outward appearance, and what others may think of us because of it, often become *all that really matters*. Ask yourself these questions:

- Do you habitually compare your body size to others?

- Do you feel good about yourself when you are the slimmest in a group?

- Do you feel bad about yourself if you are the heaviest in a group?

- Do you form opinions about people based on how fat or slim they are?

- Are you more aware of the calorie content of food than the nutritional content?

- Have you ever thought to yourself: 'If only I was slim enough I'd be confident and happy – *I would like myself more*'?

It's an illusion a great many of us have bought, even those who have given up trying. And we've bought it quite literally in terms of the products sold to us which promote thinness as a commodity like all other commodities. This is why people literally stake their lives on slimming pills and crash diets, or risk anorexia and bulimia in their struggle for a sense of self-worth.

It will help you to remember that 'looking good' brings you an illusion of self-esteem – and that's a booby prize whether you win it or lose it. This is crucial, because it affects your daily life, now. At least every time you eat.

You see, whenever you choose to eat or not to eat something, if the motivation behind your choice has to do with weight, you are thinking in terms of *false* self-esteem. If you are thinking about eating a slice of chocolate cake, for example, and you decide: 'I won't eat it because it's fattening' your motivation is very much about wanting to look more acceptable to other people.

However, if you think the solution is to say: 'I will eat it, even though I know it's fattening, because I don't care how I look' you are still thinking in terms of how you appear to others.

The alternative is to think in terms of your own opinion of yourself, but we'll get to that later.

When your body size and shape is your main consideration in your choices about food, your main concern is other people's opinions or judgements about you.

Even if you have been advised to lose weight for health reasons, the chances are there is still a strong emotional attachment to your appearance which dominates your motivation. Maybe your doctor *said*: 'Lose weight,' but what you *heard* was: 'You don't look so good in that suit.' And maybe what your doctor really *meant* was: 'Get your blood pressure down.'

You may be thinking: 'But *I* like being slim, *I* enjoy it, it pleases *me*.' Yes, I know, I do too, but wanting to be slim may be more about other people's opinions of you than you realise. Consider these questions:

- When you put on weight, isn't it when you think it's going to be noticed by other people that your heart sinks?

- When you lose weight, don't you want people to notice, even pointing it out to them if they don't make a comment?

- If you magically became your ideal weight right now, wouldn't you feel thrilled to look at yourself in a mirror? Don't mirrors show us what other people see?

- If you magically became your ideal weight right now, would you go to your next social event in the shapeless clothes you keep for when you're fat?

Weight has been so overemphasised in our culture that it's almost impossible not to be affected by it – especially for women. Think of every film you ever saw, where the skinniest, tiniest women are the central, most interesting characters. Look at any mannequin in any dress-shop window. Look at all our 'beautiful' fashion models who live dangerously close to starvation. Does this make any sense? It makes sense if you are in the business of selling false self-esteem. Then it makes very good sense, because there is no shortage of buyers.

Losing weight usually creates a 'high' from this false sense of esteem, in the same way as buying a flashy car or wearing the latest fashion does. That high can be powerful and *very* seductive, but inside, nothing's changed and you probably know it. Nothing can fool the truth inside your own heart, and in your own heart you know that having a more impressive body does nothing to improve your genuine self-esteem. As the old saying goes, all that glitters isn't gold.

It may be you have already figured this out and stopped trying to lose weight. You may be well aware that the image you present to the world does little to improve the image you have of yourself. And you may genuinely esteem yourself in ways that have nothing to do with your weight or your eating.

But still, you may have missed a very exciting opportunity. This is the opportunity to make changes in your eating, not to impress others, but in order to live your life to the full. Not so much because you will *look* your best, but because you will *feel* your best – because you will have higher *genuine* self-esteem. *You could regard your choices about eating as the way to raise your genuine self-esteem. If you do that, you may benefit in more ways than you can imagine.*

Prioritising Self-esteem

If you tend to have low self-esteem, you may be thinking: 'If only I felt better about myself, I would be able to make changes in my eating.' All you need to do is to see you've got it the wrong way round. People with low self-esteem can make huge changes – and gain self-esteem as a result. I know this because I have seen so many of my clients go through this process. You may struggle initially because you're convinced you'll fail, but it's exactly in the facing of this fear that strength and confidence in yourself will arise.

You might object to the idea of raising your level of self-esteem at all. Many people make the mistake of thinking that high self-esteem is an arrogant, inflated opinion of oneself and indifference to others. This is *not* self-esteem; in fact it is a *lack* of genuine self-esteem that leads people to become self-centred. Feeling superior is just another false esteem fix.

Or you could be someone who tends to have high self-esteem already, who rarely feels any need to prove their worth to others. This is a good place to start from, but don't let this fool you into thinking you won't benefit from taking control of overeating.

I find the words 'inner joy' helpful in describing genuine self-esteem. Can you honestly say you wouldn't want more of that? It doesn't mean you will never make mistakes. It means you won't feel quite so crushed when you do. It doesn't mean you'll feel instantly confident about facing new challenges. It does mean you're more likely to appreciate both the challenge and yourself for facing it. Most of all, it doesn't rely on other people applauding your achievements. That's nice when it happens, but it's not essential.

Genuine self-esteem comes from within; *it's very private*. This means you improve it at the same time as you let go of some of the significance of other people's opinions of you. Make your self-esteem more important to you and your weight less important. Then you are prioritising *your* opinion of yourself, rather than other people's.

Your appearance – your body shape and size – will no doubt always be significant to you, as mine is to me. What

I'm talking about here is putting it into a different perspective. The more you concern yourself with improving your own opinion of yourself, regardless of your weight, the more you will be able to stay in touch with motivation *that really works*. (1)

This still leaves the question of how to improve your genuine self-esteem, so in the next chapter we'll see what a leading authority on self-esteem has to say. This book presents just one view out of many; in it I offer you the approach that works for me, especially when it comes to taking control of overeating. My suggestion is to try it and see if it works for you.

In other words   SARAH

I had always been a couple of stone overweight, a size too big. A couple of years ago I successfully dieted to my target weight and looked and felt great. But it seemed a very brittle kind of success and the weight had crept back on over the last two years or so.

I don't think people who have never had a weight problem understand the state of mind that goes with it. I would describe myself as confident, outgoing and successful but I have always felt that I wasn't quite as good as everyone else, and attributed it to being fat. I have felt this way since I was a teenager. Yet even having dieted successfully, that feeling didn't go away.

One of the most important things I learned on the Eating Less *course was how weight is a red herring; the damage to your self-esteem is done by the overeating, not by being overweight.*

TAKING CONTROL

• It's helpful to realise that low self-esteem is often behind the low moods you might call 'having a bad day', 'feeling negative' or 'hating my life'. At times like these you may tend to think: 'If only I was slimmer, all my problems would disappear.' Raising your self-esteem may not make all your problems disappear – but it will come a lot closer to it than losing weight will!

• Whenever you think about your weight, try telling yourself:

'Having control of my overeating is more important to me than looking more acceptable to others.'

• If you lose weight, don't mention it to anyone.

• If you are getting support with your eating issues from a group or a counsellor, resist mentioning, discussing, acknowledging and especially applauding weight loss.

• If you are one of those people who compares their body size and shape to others, the next time you notice yourself doing this, remind yourself that your self-esteem has nothing to do with the size of someone else's body.

• Whenever you eat in an addictive way, be brave enough to do it in front of other people just as much as you do it on your own. This will help you to lessen the significance of other people's opinions of you when it comes to your relationship with food.

It's not that other people's opinions aren't important, it's just that it damages your own self-esteem if you make their opinions of you more important than your own.

References

1. In *Make the Connection* (Century) Oprah Winfrey and Bob Greene include a beautiful passage about this point; it explains the title of their book. Unfortunately, these few sentences are overshadowed by the preoccupation with weight loss which runs through the rest of the book:

   'The connection is a change in perception. It is first realising that losing weight is not what is most important. Instead, the excess weight is merely a symptom of a larger problem and losing weight is a side effect, a nice one certainly, of something much more important. It is really about increasing self-confidence, inner strength and discipline. It is about feeling better on a daily basis, having control over your life, and caring about yourself. Ultimately it is about self-love.

   '[When you've made the connection] you will want only the best for you, which means exercising and eating right, as well as dealing with your problems in a healthy way. You will know you've made the connection when you care enough about yourself that you don't consider doing anything outside your best interest.'

4 Motivation that Works

Dr Nathaniel Branden is a psychologist who has been studying and writing about the significance of self-esteem for over forty years. He has written about sixteen books on the subject, many of which are best-sellers and published in many parts of the world, including the US, Europe, Brazil and China.

In *The Six Pillars of Self-Esteem* he describes the six principles on which self-esteem depends:

- living consciously
- self-acceptance
- self-responsibility
- self-assertiveness
- living purposefully
- personal integrity

These are not just ideas, they are ways to live. Not as ideal states of perfection – that is unrealistic – but as directions to aim toward. The more you live by these principles, the higher your self-esteem will be. And in our relationship with food, *it is exactly the practice of these six principles that gives us the ability to take control of addictive eating.* In fact, I can't think of one thing we need to do in order to take control of an addiction that isn't on that list. When we apply these principles to our addictive behaviour, we take control and we raise our genuine self-esteem at the same time.

☐ **Living consciously**   Although nobody can be conscious of everything all the time, in general, the more aware you are the greater your ability to change your behaviour. As a simple example, if you wanted to cut down on sugar you would do better if you were aware of which foods contained sugar.

Do you know that the word 'curiosity' comes from the same root as the word 'cure'? Your curiosity leads you to your cure. It's doing it right now! It's not sufficient, however, simply to be curious; *living* consciously implies that what you discover gets put into practice.

Many aspects of addictive behaviour become automatic and therefore beyond our awareness. Each chapter in this book will help you to understand more about addiction, and will therefore bring you greater ability to take conscious control – and, as a result, raise your self-esteem.

☐ **Self-acceptance**   Self-acceptance *doesn't* mean you think everything's perfect just as it is. What it means is that you be a friend, not an enemy to yourself in pursuing your goals. Even though you dislike many aspects of overeating, have some compassion for the human being who is caught up in it. Recognising your inherent worth as a human being – *regardless of anything you do and regardless of what you look like* – will inspire you to create a way of life that reflects and honours your inherent worth.

Self-acceptance also means accepting that things are the way they are. Accept that, at least sometimes, you eat in an addictive way. Accept that it's impossible for you to continue to eat that way and maintain the best possible state of health. Accept that these things are true, no matter how much you dislike them.

☐ **Self-responsibility**   Of Dr Branden's 'six pillars', self-responsibility is likely to be the most misunderstood, especially when it comes to taking control of overeating. I suspect you may regard the notion as a dreary prospect, and the last thing you'd want to do!

In fact, taking responsibility gives you an extraordinary degree of control because it brings you the freedom to choose. *Taking responsibility is a step toward freedom, not away from it*. Chapter Six will explain much more about this and how to put it into practice.

Whenever you achieve something, it's because you take responsibility for it. Perhaps you can think of things you've accomplished simply because you stopped waiting for someone else to come along and do it for you. You paid off a debt. You finished a household project. You left a bad job. Remember the effect this had on your self-esteem.

☐ **Self-assertiveness**   Self-assertiveness is relevant when you eat with others. It can make a big difference if you start to make your own choices, at least sometimes, instead of always eating what other people want you to eat or eating something simply because everyone else is.

You may need to practise asserting yourself when people tell you how and what to eat or push you to eat when it's really not right for you to do so. You may need to talk with the person who shops and cooks for you, in order to make clear agreements about what you want.

☐ **Living purposefully**   Living purposefully means setting goals and working toward them. We'll get to what your goals about food could be later on. They won't be about weight loss; they will be about taking control of addictive eating.

☐ **Personal integrity**   If another person lied to you, made you do things you later regretted or damaged your health, you wouldn't hold them in very high esteem. When it comes to food, you may have been doing this to yourself in many ways for a long time. Often people who come to my courses tell me they regularly buy family-sized packs of chocolate bars 'for the children', only to eat them all themselves. They lie to themselves, and their self-esteem suffers as a result.

Even if you just get a bit more honest with yourself, your sense of personal integrity will soar and so will your self-esteem. It simply means doing what you believe in, doing what you say you will do, and telling the truth to yourself.

When it comes to food, do not put up with lies, or even 'white lies', such as 'Oh, just this once'. Addictive behaviour is always maintained by deceptions of various kinds. Telling the truth is your way out.

These six principles may well be familiar to you, and not only in connection with eating. And you may have practised these principles and enjoyed the benefits of healthier self-esteem when you've been in control of your eating in the past. *But it may also be that weight loss was all that really mattered to you, which invalidates these sources of genuine esteem.* Declaring that self-esteem is your main motivation behind choices about eating makes the process more deliberate. It is therefore more powerful and effective.

Whether you recognise it or not, every time you make a choice about eating there is an effect on your self-esteem. With a single choice the effect may be quite subtle, but the extraordinary thing about food is that you encounter it all the time, so you affect your self-esteem all the time. The effect is constant and cumulative.

Dr. Branden says that high self-esteem is something you can *achieve*. Making choices about eating provides you with a unique and extraordinary opportunity to achieve higher self-esteem. Your self-esteem is affected by all aspects of your life, but food has a very special significance. Not only is food a regular part of your daily life, it's also fundamental and essential to your life. Your food becomes you, so the way you relate to food leaves a more profound impression on your self-esteem than almost anything else.

Your Rewards

Learning that *you* determine your opinion of yourself, and that you have an enormous impact on your self-esteem daily, may at first seem both liberating and frightening. Many people believe that self-esteem is an inevitable consequence of childhood; that if they were invalidated by parents and teachers when they were young, they must resign themselves to low self-esteem for life. They are self-critical and believe that whatever they do, it's never enough.

Self-esteem does have its roots in the past, but it *is* possible for you to change the script. The only thing that could prevent you is your fear of the very changes you want to make. Your fear may be expressed in the familiar phrase: 'Oh, but this is me – it's just how I am!' Remember to go as slow or as fast as you want; it's not a race. Get support if you want to. You have the rest of your life to work on this, and even small steps can produce exciting results.

Not only will your relationship with food improve, but by applying these principles to eating, you will increase their significance in your life. In taking control of your overeating you take more control of your life in general. By becoming more at peace with your eating you become more at peace with yourself. In gaining a healthy relationship with food you improve your relationships with everyone – especially yourself.

And for many people, raising self-esteem will be the only way to make 'looking good' lose some of its significance. You may have believed for much of your life that your worth as a person is determined by the size of your body, and you'll find that things really start to change when you give up trying to prove your self-worth in this way. Since it doesn't generate genuine self-esteem anyway, *it's never enough*, even when you do receive approval from others.

This is an arena that provides you with opportunities like no other. Begin by treating yourself as if you are more worthy, regardless of your size, and before too long you will feel more worthy, regardless of your size. Simply pay attention to all the ways your life improves when you are in control of your eating:

Benefits you gain from raising your level of self-esteem

- inner strength and confidence, rather than feeling like a victim of life

- inner joy and peace, which is less dependent on external circumstances
- feeling more at ease with yourself, either when you're alone or with others
- feeling grounded and centred
- productivity and enthusiasm for life
- less dependent and therefore more satisfying relationships
- greater ability to trust yourself and your own thinking
- creativity, because you believe in yourself more
- less sensitivity to criticism
- less self-consciousness and anxiety
- less need to be defensive, competitive or judgmental
- greater ability to recover from other compulsive behaviours such as smoking or working
- greater ability to cope with major life changes, such as death of relative, end of relationship, redundancy or retirement

Benefits you gain from taking control of overeating, in addition to higher self-esteem and weight loss

- taking control of your life, instead of being controlled by your addictive appetite
- greater enjoyment of eating, free from guilt, regrets, fear or anxiety
- vitality and sustained energy, feeling more alive
- becoming more emotionally balanced and feeling more positive
- a social life free from preoccupation with food
- freedom from bloated, uncomfortable feelings from eating too much

- freedom from diets
- freedom to cook anything for others, knowing you don't have to eat it
- clearer thinking, better concentration and improved attention span
- savings in money and time
- greater adaptability to seasonal temperature changes
- reduced susceptibility to symptoms of stress
- better health

I could list all the physical ailments connected with addictive eating, but I can't think of many health problems that *aren't* affected by the food we eat. It's vital to acknowledge that the ongoing maladies you may suffer from – such as fatigue, infections, constipation, diarrhoea, haemorrhoids, premenstrual tension, stomach aches and clogged sinuses – are in almost all cases preventable and treatable by the quality and quantity of the food you eat. Even serious conditions such as high blood pressure, late-onset diabetes, heart disease, strokes, arthritis and cancer are often directly linked with addictive eating. (1)

Many people believe these illnesses are determined by the luck of their genes, and it is true that we do tend to inherit the same genetic 'Achilles heel' as other members of our family. What this means, though, is that in one family overeating usually leads to diabetes, while in another it usually leads to heart disease or a particular kind of cancer, and in another to arthritis, and so on.

By taking control of your overeating you will at the very least delay the onset of these conditions, and you could avoid them all together. Many factors work together to create illness, including stress, genes, inactivity and environment. Certainly our minds and emotions play no small part. Food is also a very significant factor – and as a habitual overeater this may well be the last thing you want to acknowledge.

Have we strayed off the subject of self-esteem here? No. When you value your physical health, your self-esteem rises, just as eating in a way that could harm your health undermines it.

How Not to Sabotage Yourself

Even after all this, I suspect I still haven't fully convinced you. I am well aware of the allure of 'looking good'. If you think you could look like a film star, and I'm just offering you self-esteem, what are you most likely to use to motivate yourself? You might just bargain: 'OK, OK, I'll go for the self-esteem if it will help me lose weight'!

The attraction of weight loss as your main goal can be even stronger if you are very overweight. You may not want to look like a star, just a 'normal' person who doesn't get rude stares everywhere they go. Even so, prioritising weight loss can lead you off track.

You may lose some weight, but chances are you will sabotage yourself in some way if your self-esteem remains low. People who dislike themselves often punish themselves by doing things they know they will regret later on. This self-destructive behaviour lowers their self-esteem even more. This may sound all too familiar: 'I'm fat, so I'm worthless, so I might as well eat more, so I overeat, then I feel guilty, and I get fatter, which proves I'm worthless, so I might as well eat.'

This vicious circle is driven by exaggerated, inappropriate guilt: the hallmark of low self-esteem. In the past you may have tried to break the cycle by trying to lose weight. *But if you measure your worth by your body size, it may be a long time before you feel any better about yourself, so you are more likely to return to overeating.* Weight loss is slow. But you can benefit from applying Dr Branden's 'six pillars' immediately.

You can apply the practice of the 'six pillars' – living consciously, self-acceptance, self-responsibility, self-assertiveness, living purposefully and personal integrity – specifically to food, whatever your appearance. You break the cycle by raising your self-esteem. When you apply these principles to your eating your self-esteem will improve long before you achieve any significant weight loss.

In order to do this, though, you need to start out by stressing motivation that is about anything other than your weight, shape and size. *Look for any reason to make changes in your eating other than your appearance.*

When I keep in mind the impact my eating has on my self-esteem, I don't overeat because I know the rewards of not doing so are precious. I become significantly happier, regardless of external circumstances in my life. I can't think of anything else that has as much impact on my self-esteem as my eating. Not my weight. My *eating*.

That's what works for me. Just try it, and see if it works for you. If it doesn't, you can discard it. It doesn't have to be a permanent commitment.

You are more likely to take control of your addictive eating if you are going to get something you really want out of it. Whether it's drinking, smoking, overeating or whatever, the most compelling aspect of any addiction is that it brings you pleasure. If you try to limit this pleasure in order to please or impress others, it becomes an act of self-sacrifice. It's very difficult to stay motivated to keep sacrificing yourself. Not only that, but your motivation is dependent on how others are treating you. If they let you down, the thing to do *for yourself* will be to return to addictive eating. *To make a lasting change, you will need to find more pleasure in controlling your eating than in overeating. Otherwise you won't stay with it.*

In other words   **MARGARET**

I'm eating about half the amount I used to before I did the Eating Less *course. My digestive problems seem to have sorted themselves out. I used to suffer with heartburn and feelings of nausea almost every time I ate, and these have pretty much disappeared, mainly, I think, from eating a lot less fat. Also, I used to eat about every two hours. Now I feel better eating after at least four hours.*

I have a more positive attitude in general and a lot more energy; it's like a stress has been lifted. It's a mental state that has changed. I'm not depressed about my eating any more and I don't feel so helpless. I had resigned myself to getting heavier and heavier and never being able to do anything about it. All kinds of social events are a lot less stressful now because I don't feel desperate about being at parties and stuffing myself with food.

TAKING CONTROL

• List, in as much detail as you can, what it means to you to be in control of your eating and what it costs you to be out of control. Put the emphasis on eating rather than weight. If you tend to ignore or invalidate these less concrete benefits, spend some time thinking about what this means to you. Keep the list somewhere safe, private and easily accessible, like a Filofax, a diary or a jewellery box. Refer to it often, adding to it as you go along.

• Don't tell other people about your triumphs and successes in taking control of your overeating. By keeping this to yourself you begin to break down some of your dependency on other people's approval. Get used to feeling your pride in your accomplishments, acknowledging the effect on your own self-esteem – privately.

• When you do lose some weight, it's inevitable and very understandable that you'll feel delighted. However, it helps to resist wearing clothes that emphasise and show off your new shape and size, at least for a while. Remind yourself of the benefits other than body size. Your addictive eating is likely to increase if you don't keep the focus on self-esteem.

I'm not suggesting you should never wear smaller sizes. I'm suggesting you take things very slowly. Changing your body shape is a big thing to do. Ease into it gradually, make it as insignificant as you possibly can, and it's much more likely to last.

References

1. 'Possibly the greatest misconception people have about the process
    of aging is that it's synonymous with illness . . . There are two
    principal factors responsible for the onset and severity of most
    chronic and degenerative conditions – your genetic heritage, which
    you cannot control; and your lifestyle, which you can and should
    control.

    'The goal of our program is to maintain vitality into old age. It
    grew out of the realisation that there are specific types of exercise
    and eating patterns that can greatly diminish the chances that
    people will develop a chronic disease; or if they're already
    suffering from one, could help them escape from the imprisonment
    of its debilitating symptoms.'
    From *Biomarkers: The 10 Keys to Prolong Vitality* by Drs Evans and
    Rosenberg (Simon & Schuster).

5   What Is Addiction?

I'm aware that I've been using the word 'addiction' without saying much about what addiction is. So let's look at what an addiction is made of, because understanding it will help you deal with it.

Not everyone agrees that food is addictive. My conviction that people do become addicted to food has come from my experience of helping people to stop smoking. Smokers frequently smoke instead of eat, and, especially when stopping smoking, eat instead of smoke. Tobacco is widely accepted as being addictive, and for many people the impulse to smoke and the impulse to eat become interchangeable and even at times indistinguishable. By saying food is addictive we don't create a problem, but face the truth of an existing one.

Even so, calling food an addiction raises many more questions than it answers. First, here is a list of things people usually think of as being addictive: alcohol, nicotine, heroin, methadone, cocaine, cannabis, solvents, caffeine, tranquillisers, amphetamines, exercise, television, computer games, computers, working, gambling, sex, shopping – and food, especially chocolate and all the processed foods that contain refined sugar, refined flour, fats and/or salt.

This isn't a complete list, but it's enough for us to begin to get a picture. Each one, of course, has its own particular characteristics. Food addiction is not the same as gambling addiction. Being a smoker is not the same as being a compulsive shopper. What's important is the characteristics they share that make them addictions, at least sometimes for some people. Let's see what those characteristics are and how they apply to food.

Aspects of Addiction

☐ **Addictive desire** – *'I want it.'*
Perhaps the most obvious characteristic of addiction is a concept so familiar we have many words to describe it: desire, craving, compulsion, urge, yearning, longing, anticipation and even obsession. When you are addicted to something, you want it. You are attracted to it.

It is this desire that makes your behaviour difficult to control, and leads to relapses. This is implicit in the idea of addiction: addictive behaviour is something you have difficulty *not* doing because at the same time as wanting to stop doing it, you also want to do it!

The addictive desire is a 'conditioned response', which means you automatically associate your addiction with certain cues. For example, if I eat popcorn every time I go to the cinema, I condition myself to expect popcorn whenever I go to the cinema. My memory produces the conditioned response – the addictive desire – whether or not I'm naturally hungry.

The conditioned response is a major factor in all addictions, but it's especially important in dealing with smoking and eating because the cues are so thoroughly integrated into our daily lives.

☐ **Cost** – *'It's bad for me.'*
When we call something an addiction we imply there's a problem of some kind. There's a cost in continuing to satisfy our addictive desire, in terms of health, wealth and self-esteem. We may be addicted to things that are good for us, such as food or exercise, but the part of the behaviour we call 'addiction' is, *by definition*, the part that is detrimental in some way.

Addictions never contribute to our well-being. Essentials such as sleeping, although repeated daily all through our lives, aren't called addictions. We genuinely need to sleep, so there's no problem. In fact, we have problems if we don't sleep.

Sooner or later the cost of the addiction is too high and the addict starts trying to control the behaviour. When addictive behaviour continues despite the cost, guilt becomes an added problem.

The cost isn't just the 'downside'. It actually adds power to the addiction, making it more attractive. The danger and illegality of drugs make them more interesting for some people than they would otherwise be. Food addiction may look innocent, but the same mechanism is at work: it becomes 'naughty fun' if it's forbidden in some way.

Extra weight is usually the most obvious cost of food addiction, but, as I hope I've established in preceding chapters, it will serve you to become aware of the other things you inevitably sacrifice in the pursuit of your 'fix'.

☐ **Pleasure** – *'I love it.'*
The satisfaction of our addictive desire usually brings us pleasure, and, of course, pleasure is very much a matter of personal preference. I can't think of much that's less pleasurable than gambling, but there may well be compulsive gamblers who are indifferent to chocolate-covered raisins.

Addiction lives in the world of sensation. It is often supported by a hedonistic view of life: that the pursuit of pleasure is the highest good. It's fuelled by a sense of excitement, satisfaction or reward. This is why we have the addictive desire: we tend to want to repeat the things we enjoy.

There can come a time when the addict derives no pleasure from their addiction because the cost has become too overwhelming, but at some time in the development of the addiction, pleasure was involved. By the way, this distinguishes addiction from 'obsessive-compulsive disorder' (OCD). An example of OCD is compulsive hand-washing, and the main reason this is not thought of as addiction is that there's no pleasure involved at any point. The person with OCD doesn't think: 'I can't wait to get home and get some of that lovely sandalwood soap all over my hands.'

When it comes to dealing with food addiction, one difficulty is that pleasure and satisfaction are perfectly normal, appropriate and even necessary responses to eating food. This gives credibility to the familiar justification for overeating: 'I enjoy my food – what's wrong with that?' The challenge is to recognise the difference between appropriate enjoyment and the satisfaction of addictive desire.

☐ **Altered state of consciousness** – *'It cheers me up.'*
To varying degrees, addictions temporarily change the way we think and feel; they make us high, drugged, 'absent-minded' or numbed in some way. Overeaters can go into a kind of daze even while eating a perfectly ordinary meal. A food binge can create a state of intoxication or stupor not unlike that produced by alcohol.

This altered state of consciousness can create a buffer between us and our feelings, and this brings us a sense of comfort, which is why we often turn to our addictions when we are unhappy or stressed. A number of books on overeating focus on this exclusively as the cause of overeating, but you probably know already that you also eat addictively even when you are happy. Satisfying our addictive desire usually brings us pleasure and comfort. There aren't many circumstances in which we don't want that.

☐ **Secondary conditioning** – *'I love everything about it.'*
Not only do we get pleasure from the addiction, but also from all kinds of things directly associated with it. Heroin addicts can get as much excitement from procuring their drug and preparing it for use as in taking it. Some alcoholics thoroughly enjoy their active social life only because it's integral to their drinking; without the booze the friends would be worthless.

In the same way, shopping for food, preparation of food and social events which include eating carry a special significance for the addicted eater. Food could be your hobby and even your career.

Again, the difficulty with food addiction is that it all seems so completely natural. It's important, though, to see what this addiction is made of. It's made up of the same things as other addictions.

□ **Interaction of body and mind** – *'I need it.'*
Many people believe that addictive behaviour is caused by body chemistry. An addictive desire to eat is often experienced as a physical feeling, so it's easy to assume that if it's felt in the body, it's created in the body. But this isn't necessarily the case. A great many physical sensations arise from states of mind: emotions such as anger and disappointment, stage fright and panic attacks, to name but a few examples. (1)

□ **Susceptibility** – *'My whole family's prone to it.'*
Everybody's body is different. We aren't all born with the potential to become world-class athletes, opera singers – or alcoholics. We work with what we're given.

What we may have been given is a predisposition to become addicted to things in general, and we may have been given a predisposition to become addicted to food. Research is not conclusive on this, but one Stanford University study showed that a quarter of an otherwise normal, healthy population produce too much insulin in response to carbohydrates. (2)

This could be a physical factor in addictive eating, but remember it's just one part of the whole picture. It doesn't mean you can't make lasting changes.

□ **Exposure** – *'Everyone's doing it.'*
Before we can take up a particular addiction we must have access to it, and the more widespread it is in our community, the more likely we are to get involved. If all my friends smoke I am more likely to join in, especially if I'm young.

Of course most of us have access to too much food and poor quality food, but some social groups encourage its consumption. You may be part of a family or group of friends that takes addictive eating for granted, perhaps even regarding it as healthy, for example, when people say: 'He's got a healthy appetite'.

This doesn't mean you can't do anything about your own eating. Just don't try to change theirs! What may be required is for you to assert yourself, saying: 'No, thanks' instead of succumbing to peer pressure. When you take decisions that are right for you, notice the effect this has on your self-esteem.

Our culture encourages addictive eating. The food industry is chiefly concerned with marketing its products, which usually means promoting the more addictive foods – processed products high in fats, sugar, flour and salt – rather than health. 'Health' is a good marketing strategy, but is rarely, if ever, much more than that.

Advertising and availability make addictive junk food seem 'normal'. As a result a great many of us are confused about food, unable to appreciate or even care about the essential difference between a bag of crisps and an apple, for example. (3)

Just because something is considered acceptable within a culture or group, doesn't mean it isn't addictive behaviour. In many parts of the world it is considered normal to smoke, and so many people smoke it's considered odd if you don't. This doesn't mean the smokers are not addicted, it just means that this particular society has a different attitude towards this addiction.

Your social group may consider it normal to eat a portion of chips every day for lunch. Your family may think it perfectly normal to eat a sweet and fatty pudding after every meal. I was raised in such a family. Just because everybody around you does it, this doesn't mean it isn't addictive eating.

You might encounter another kind of peer pressure: endless conversations about weight and dieting. If you have a friend or group of friends with whom you discuss these issues, this may be another aspect to your addiction, because it keeps you focused on weight. Start to think of ways to remove yourself from these conversations.

☐ **Withdrawal symptoms** – *'It's awful when I stop.'*
Withdrawal symptoms are the negative, difficult or unpleasant things that happen when you stop the addictive behaviour. Symptoms are often thought of as purely physical, but there is also a psychological side to withdrawal, which is more significant.

The physical side can look like illness, but it's just recovery from the abuse of the addiction. With food, health and nutrition expert Leslie Kenton speaks of 'cleansing reactions' to a detoxification diet in her *10 Day Clean-Up Plan*:

> Such reactions can include headaches, muscle or joint pains, sensitivity, tiredness . . . due to the rapid mobilisation and release of stored toxins and wastes. [Your body] is working very hard to clean and renew itself.

It's possible, though, that we don't have to do a detox diet to experience withdrawal symptoms from food. It could be that a whole range of ailments are really withdrawal symptoms from whatever addictive junk food we consumed the previous day. We may regard our aches, low energy and inability to concentrate as permanent and inevitable features of our lives, only seeing their connection with food when we make changes in our eating.

Far more important for us are the changes we need to make in our thinking. Taking control of overeating, as any other addiction, is a major change. You don't do something like that without an inner struggle, one that takes time and effort. *Psychological withdrawal is the difficulty in making a real change, and it's an essential part of the process.*

☐ **Tolerance** – *'I've got a big appetite and a sweet tooth.'*
The body can adapt to and endure the abuse we inflict on it. We could take small amounts of poison, gradually increase the dose and eventually survive what would otherwise, on the first try, be fatal. Tolerance means we get used to unnatural substances, which is why doses usually increase.

People may start smoking only one or two cigarettes a day, but over time increase to twenty or thirty a day. The body becomes tolerant of nicotine and more is required in order to achieve the same effect. If a non-smoker tried to smoke thirty in one day, he would feel absolutely dreadful – because he hasn't built up any tolerance to tobacco.

With food addiction, our stomachs expand so we can tolerate larger amounts. We also develop tolerance for the quality of food. People often say their taste-buds change after they have been eating different kinds of food for a while. Large amounts of sugar and fat, for example, don't appeal as much as they once did because the person's tolerance for them has faded.

☐ **Justification** – *'Life's too short'* – **and Denial** – *'It's not going to kill me.'*

All addictions are supported by ways of thinking which become so ingrained that it can be tough to separate the truth in them from the illusion. These beliefs work hand in hand to justify satisfying the addictive desire and to deny: (a) that you're eating addictively in the first place, and (b) even if you are, that it's bad for you in any way.

Justification and denial are such a powerful part of addiction that it's essential to break their hold by rigorous truth-telling. After all, if your life will fall apart without it, and it isn't doing you any harm, why would you ever stop doing it?

Justification and denial are attempts to feel OK about the addiction. Whenever the denial is challenged – when you get ill, for example – the clearer it becomes that the addiction is harmful, the more you will rely on your justifications, and the more convincing they will need to be. This tends to create some fear at the thought of taking control of the addiction, because you believe you are dependent on it in some significant way.

This doesn't mean the justifications and the fear they create are your best guides to making wise decisions. Facing the fear is always part of the process because it's only by facing fear that you can overcome it. We'll look at justifications in more detail in Chapters Nine and Ten.

As an example of denial, one client, Janet, swore she couldn't think of a single reason to cut back on her over-eating other than her weight. She thought and thought, and looked at me as if I were mad to suggest such a silly idea. However, just two weeks earlier, she had cancelled a session because of a migraine which, she had told me, was brought on by overeating the day before. Her addicted mind had simply ignored this evidence.

Denial is tricky to overcome because the whole point of it is that the truth is hidden from you. It's safe to assume, though, that there is some degree of denial in any addictive behaviour. (4)

Take note of any physical symptoms of ill health you have, especially persistent ones. Is it possible they have anything to do with either the quality or the quantity of the food you eat? Look at any persistent emotional and relationship problems you have. You might think of these problems as the *cause* of overeating, but in fact they may be the *result*. (I am referring here to the effect overeating has on your self-esteem, not your weight. People with low self-esteem tend to get depressed and also to create problematic 'co-dependent' relationships.)

As well as the truths you keep hidden from yourself, denial usually involves hiding things from other people. Most addicts keep crucial details of their addictions secret; they may even try to keep the whole addiction secret, especially from certain people. Of course, it's difficult to hide the effects of addictive eating, which is why so many overeaters become obsessed with weight loss: it's evidence that other people can see.

☐ **Conflict of values** – *'I'm not always sure I want to eat less.'*
Practising an addiction means you make one value (satisfying the addiction) more important than another value (being in good health). When you make your self-esteem the purpose behind taking control of overeating, you create a new priority in your values: *I* matter here, the quality of *my* life matters, my health matters – to *me*. This doesn't happen automatically, and it may not feel natural at first. You need to make deliberate choices to change things, and at first you may feel ambivalent, as if torn in two directions.

The process of breaking free from any addiction is resolving this conflict by choosing to change your priorities. This is crucial, because any addiction is strengthened by the confusion and inconsistency of purpose which surround it.

☐ **Action** – *'It's what I do.'*
For me, one of the most fascinating aspects of addictions is that they involve behaviour – things you do. However hard

you try, you can't get away from the fact of the actions you
have or have not taken. You could affirm your commitment
to your health over and over again, but if you then follow
that with the act of addictive eating, your self-esteem will
suffer.

This can be a hard lesson to learn, but it has its bright side.
If done correctly, changing your actions – your behaviour –
has tremendous psychological and spiritual rewards. As a
friend of mine likes to say: 'Often it's better to act your way
into right thinking than to think your way into right acting.'

Addiction to Food

To sum up: an addiction is a problem, which is why, sooner
or later, we want to stop doing it. But it's also something we
are very familiar with, which seems to comfort us and bring
us pleasure, so we are 'in two minds' about what to do.
Addiction involves certain actions, but these actions are
supported by ways of thinking which are an integral part of
the addiction.

What distinguishes overeating from almost all other
addictions is its ability to be comparatively invisible. This is
because it is easily confused with the eating we do which is
not addictive because it's completely necessary. Someone
trying to stop smoking, for example, can at least clearly
identify what it is they are trying to stop doing. Anyone
addicted to food knows it's as addictive as any drug, but
can't see exactly where their addiction begins and ends.

Some people have attempted to define food addiction by
classifying certain kinds of food as addictive, such as sugar
and white flour. They advocate abstention from these, using
this criterion as a way of defining addiction.

If you want to abstain completely from specific foods
(perhaps you already do) because of addiction, religion,
health, or any other reason, you can use everything in this
book to support you in that goal. However, I don't advocate
complete abstinence from any foods as the solution for
everybody. (I heard you breathe a sigh of relief there!)

We still don't have a definition of addictive eating, however. Our first images, perhaps, are the most dramatic and obvious. It's a midnight binge ... spoonfuls of creamy, sugary goo consumed in a semi-conscious daze ... It's eating when you are depressed or angry ... It's eating between meals or eating too quickly ... It's eating chocolate or going back for second helpings or thirds ... It's eating standing up or watching TV.

Remember, though, that one characteristic common to all addictions is that they are not essential for normal living. Non-addictive eating, pleasurable as it is and should be, is eating food in order to stay alive and in good health.

I propose a different, perhaps radical, definition of food addiction. *Food addiction is eating anything other than what your body needs to stay in good health.* You might eat more food than your body needs at meals, in snacks between meals or both. It's addictive if it's more than you need. Extra weight is a good clue: it can tell you that you've been overeating. But it's not an inevitable result; it's possible to stay slim eating very addictive foods you don't need at all.

Food addiction has two aspects. One is quantity: you're eating more food than you need, whether it's healthy or not. The other is quality: you're eating things you don't need at all because of their poor nutritional content (and even anti-nutritional content – things you would be much better off without).

So what is it that we need to eat in order to stay in the best possible health? We'll look at this in more detail later on, but to give you a rough idea: between 1,500 and 2,000 calories a day, depending on your age and level of physical activity. Those calories would be obtained from food that is as close to its natural state as possible. (5)

Now the good news: *I do not suggest that you completely eliminate addictive eating.* I do know, however, that you can control it – and before you can control it you need to know what it is. Our goal is first to know when we may be about to eat addictively, and then to develop the ability to do it less and less often.

In order to do this we need to take a closer look at the way an addiction works, which we'll do in the next four chapters.

In other words   SARAH

I daren't think how many hours of my life I must have wasted obsessing about food, calorie counting, resisting chocolate, eating something I don't really want 'to cheer myself up', feeling guilty, weighing myself, eating something else I don't really want 'because I'm bored', hunting for clothes that don't make me look fat, complaining to my friends that it's just not fair.

Now I'm free to get on with my real life of friends and work and interests and family without the fuzz of food addiction clouding everything. I have, incidentally, lost weight and dropped a dress size.

TAKING CONTROL

• Next time you want to eat something, and you are fairly sure it isn't a natural hunger, wait a while, it doesn't matter how long, before going ahead and eating. It's likely you'll really want to eat. This is an experience of the addictive desire. Observe the desire, and what it feels like to you, even if it's just for a few moments. Notice your own experience, rather than trying to fit it into a picture you may have about what an addictive desire to eat should be.

• Start to take note (mental and/or written) of your addictive desire and your justifications for overeating. You may find this difficult at first, partly because you may judge yourself for these things and partly because the addiction wants to keep them all hidden. An addiction is always supported by lies, and when you expose a lie it's difficult to maintain. That's the point. The more you push yourself to do it, the easier it will become.

Try not to judge yourself too harshly. Most people are addicted to something – caffeine, for example. Instead of condemning yourself, you could congratulate yourself for starting to do something about it – and appreciate yourself for all the things you are *not* addicted to!

• As you read on, it's likely you'll have some concerns about what all this will lead to in the future. What will your life be like if you get involved with this technique? Will you be able to cope with parties, family gatherings and holidays? And will you continue to use the Eating Less techniques even though you've given up on things you've tried before? You may even find that the thought of success (whatever that means to you) is just as frightening as predicting failure.

Be careful, because although worries such as these are perfectly normal and understandable, they can easily turn into the self-fulfilling prophecy: 'I'll never be able to keep this up, so why bother trying in the first place?'

Counter this thinking by simply bringing yourself back to the here and now. Remind yourself that the future hasn't happened yet: it only exists in your fantasies about it. The more you stay focused on the present time – whatever is happening right now – the easier it will be for you to stay positive and motivated about any changes you may want to make.

You don't have to believe that this approach will work for you in order for it to work. In any case, you are unlikely to know until you've tried it. Be willing to not know what will happen, and see what unfolds.

References

1. In his book *Timeless Healing: The Power and Biology of Belief*, Dr Herbert Benson, President of the Harvard Medical School's Mind/Body Medical Institute, describes phantom pregnancy (called 'pseudocyesis') in which physical changes are created by the mind:

   'In this condition, menstruation stops and abdominal swelling occurs at a rate similar to that of a normal pregnancy. Breasts grow larger and more tender, and nipples change pigment as is consistent with pregnancy. Nipples also increase in size and milk is secreted. Some women feel what they think is fetal movement during the fourth or fifth month of a false pregnancy.'

If a desire for a baby can produce all that, surely an addictive desire for food can create a physical sensation of hunger!

2. This study is referred to in *The Zone* by Barry Sears, Ph.D. (HarperCollins).

3. A major study of the eating habits of eleven thousand people over a period of seventeen years revealed a significant link between a longer, healthier life and the consumption of fruit. No other food was found to have such a significant effect. Regular fruit eaters had a twenty-four per cent reduction in deaths from heart disease, a thirty-two per cent reduction in deaths from strokes and a twenty-one per cent reduction in deaths from other causes. (Reported in *The British Medical Journal* (1996; 313: 755–779).)

4. If my experience with clients is anything to go by, a great many people are not fully aware of the effect food has on their health. An article in the *Independent* (July 24, 1997) reported that, according to the findings of the National Heart Forum, Britain has the worst heart disease death rates in the Western world:

'Heart attacks do not come out of the blue. More than 90 per cent of them have at least one factor – raised blood pressure, raised cholesterol or smoking – which at least doubles the risk . . . The average diet is a disaster and the average level of physical activity is totally inadequate. We need to make dramatic changes, not just fiddle around the edges.'

5. A number of writers on health and nutrition speak of the positive effect eating less has on our health. Leslie Kenton, in her book *The New Ultrahealth*, refers to a number of different studies which support this, including the following:

'Dr Alexander Leaf from Harvard Medical School spent several years studying three cultures where the people were exceptionally long lived . . . but who at the same time showed few signs of degenerative changes traditionally associated with age . . . They suffered neither tooth decay, heart disease, mental illness, obesity nor cancer . . . they led extremely active lives, regardless of their age, and had vigorous sex lives well into their eighties and nineties . . . They ate a very low-calorie diet. While the average Briton or American eats somewhere between 3,000 and 3,500 calories a day . . . they ate a mere 1,700 . . . low in fats and in proteins from animal sources and high in fresh foods, a great many of them eaten raw . . . they had never heard of sugar. . . .'

Barry Sears puts it quite simply in *The Zone*: '. . . the best way to retard aging is to restrict calories, but not essential nutrients.'

And, in *The Optimum Nutrition Bible*, Patrick Holford states: 'It is more likely that the leaner you are the longer you will live. . . . It is about giving your body exactly what it needs and no more.'

6 The Freedom to Choose

No one can control something they aren't responsible for. This is why attempts to control addictive eating which lack this quality fail so miserably, and even reinforce the addictive behaviour. On the other hand, when you begin to take even a bit more responsibility, you will find that things really start to change.

In this chapter we'll look at how you can become more responsible, which is often not at all obvious. First of all, let's look at a situation in which you wouldn't be eating addictively, but for which you wouldn't be responsible.

Imagine for a moment that somebody else has control of your food, so they decide when, what and how much you eat. They give you just enough food to stay alive and healthy and no more, and you don't have access to any other food. Of course this could only be accomplished if they had restrained you in some way, if you were locked up in a cell from which there was no escape. Otherwise you'd be free to run off and eat whatever you wanted.

How do you think you'd react in that situation? My guess is you would have a mixture of two completely different reactions. One would be compliance, and the other would be some kind of rebellion.

Compliance would mean going along with the way things are, even feeling grateful for being locked up because, finally, you were not overeating. You might feel relieved and try your best to conform and to 'be good'.

Rebellion could take many different forms. You might be rude and uncooperative towards your jailers. If they wanted you to keep your cell tidy, you might rebel by messing it up.

You might start to dig a secret tunnel or look for some other way to get out, by becoming ill, for example.

Your rebellion would be fuelled by your anger and resentment over the injustice of not being free to eat whatever you wanted. And when you were finally let out, you'd most likely devour all the things you hadn't been allowed to eat before. This is what you might call 'being bad'.

Different personalities will identify with one of these reactions more than the other, but the chances are you would experience them both in varying degrees as time went on. On one day in your cell you might think: 'Oh, this is great. Look at all the weight I'm losing.' But on another day all you would think about is your favourite 'comfort foods' and how much you wanted them and missed them – especially if you could smell them and see other people eating them!

This scenario illustrates how you are affected by the degree to which you take responsibility for your eating. If you are locked up in the cell as I just described, you are not responsible for the quantity or the quality of the food you eat. Your jailer is.

The point is that whenever people try to eat less, they invariably mimic this situation in their minds. They create a mental attitude that imitates being locked up in a cell with only enough food to survive. This is because they don't take responsibility.

It is this that creates the cycle of alternately dieting and bingeing that so many people find themselves caught up in. They lock themselves into a diet, comply with the rules for as long as they can, then make up for lost time as soon as they've been 'released' – when they've reached a target weight, for example.

Whether you've ever followed diets or not, the chances are you can identify with this to some degree. Any attempt to cut back on addictive eating is usually carried out through a denial of choice, and a denial of choice is a denial of responsibility. Maybe you say to yourself: 'I *can't* have any more' or 'That's *forbidden*' or 'I'm *not allowed* to eat anything with sugar in' or 'I *mustn't* eat between meals' or 'I've *got to* stop eating so much.'

Most people fear that if they have the freedom to overeat, they will.
So in order to take control they must deny themselves that freedom.

With thoughts like these, there's only one way to go:
comply for as long as you can, and then rebel. Compliance
may look like control, but after living for some time with this
kind of prohibitive thinking, it will feel like deprivation.
Eventually, even the thought of compliance feels like
deprivation, which is why many people overeat just before
starting a diet. *This is a very big part of addictive eating. It's*
eating more food than you need so that you don't feel deprived.

But how much you feel deprived has very little to do with
how much you are or are not eating. I'm not talking about
physical deprivation in the sense of famine, malnutrition or
starvation. These feelings of deprivation come from a state of
mind. That state of mind is one of resentment, created by
believing you are prohibited from eating something, that you
are restricted, or bound by certain rules. It's created from
thinking things like: 'I have to,' 'I must,' 'I'm not allowed,' 'I
can't' and 'I never will again.'

Something that happened to me recently is one example of
how this works. As part of my research for this book I read
some leaflets – the kind available at the doctor's – to see
what was the official advice on nutrition these days. One of
these leaflets was about keeping your heart in good shape,
and it listed foods that contribute to heart disease. On this
list was 'pork pies'. I read it and then forgot all about it. I'm
not a big pork-pie eater; I may have one or two a year. But a
few days later in the supermarket I found myself drawn to a
shelf full of – you guessed it – pork pies! I really wanted one,
but I was also curious about this sudden interest in something I don't usually buy. Then I remembered the leaflet.
Without realising, I had recorded pork pies as 'forbidden'
and the rebel in me showed up as predictably as day follows
night.

If I had then reacted by telling myself: 'Don't you dare eat
one of those!' I believe I would have made things worse,
because then I would have felt deprived and wanted one
even more. Instead, I gave myself permission to eat all the

pork pies I wanted – remembering what the consequences of doing so would be. I gave myself a choice, and in doing so I took responsibility.

The position I take is: 'This is my body and it's up to me what goes in it. I'm in charge here. Health experts give me helpful information, but I choose whether or not to follow their advice.'

If I don't take that step, all I can do is rebel, or comply for a while and then rebel all the more. *The more I take responsibility by recognising my freedom to choose, the less I feel deprived and the less I need to rebel.*

When it comes to taking control of addiction, it makes all the difference when people genuinely take responsibility for the choices they make. Any addictive behaviour is by its very nature irresponsible, so breaking free from addiction is inevitably a process of taking more and more responsibility.

After all, you can't be in control of something if you're not responsible for it. *This is the key: take responsibility and, as a result, you take control.*

Signs of Denial of Choice

☐ **Language** – '*I mustn't . . .*'
Become aware of the language you use, in your private thoughts and when you speak to others. What sort of things do you say to yourself? Do you use prohibitive language? Diets inevitably include a list of 'forbidden' or 'banned' foods, and diet books tell you what you are 'allowed' to eat, what you 'can't' eat and what you 'must not' or 'have to' do. If you aren't aware of this language and the powerful effect it has, it's easy to assimilate it into your own thinking. When this happens it's as if you are being made to follow orders, as if someone else is in control of you – and your addicted mind will react to that.

Making threats to yourself – 'You'd better not eat that' or 'Don't you dare' – will have the same effect. This language imitates your jailer, who gives you commands, with threats if they aren't obeyed. So you end up feeling like you have no

DEPRIVATION OR CHOICE

If you try to eat less by telling yourself:

I can't...   I mustn't...   I shouldn't...   I won't...
I have to stop...   I've got to stop...   I'm not allowed...
I'm not able to...   It's forbidden...   I never will again...

*You'll react as if
you were locked up
and forced to eat less:*

Either you comply:

Be good and follow the rules
Eat less food
Feel happy and grateful
Don't eat junk food
Lose weight
Feel relieved and successful

Or you rebel:

Feel deprived, angry, resentful
Feel miserable and martyred
Can't stop thinking about food
Feel guilty about eating
Eat compulsively whenever a
good excuse comes along

Compliance looks good - but it leads to rebellion sooner or later

The solution is to tell yourself:

This is my choice.
I can eat anything I want.
I can eat as much as I want.

- Say these things to yourself whenever you think about eating something, while you are eating and when you've finished - *especially* if it's addictive eating.

- Fear of failure makes free choice difficult to grasp. The fear is: 'If I really can eat anything I want, I know I will.' Then what follows is a denial of free choice in an attempt to eat less.

- You always have free choices, no matter what the consequences of those choices may be. A bad choice is still a choice. With each choice, either to eat or not to eat something, you choose:
  Either to enhance your health.
  Or to undermine your health.

- When you know you have choices, then - *and only then* - you are taking responsibility. Take responsibility and you take control.

choice but to obey. Even if you know it's you who's doing the commanding, you'll still react as if you are being told what to do.

There are other ways of avoiding responsibility through the language you use, such as the expression: 'I found myself . . .' as in 'I found myself in the kitchen eating the rest of the cake.' No, you didn't! First of all, you thought about the unfinished cake, then you made choices to walk into your kitchen, get the cake out of the cupboard, put it on a plate, take the plate and sit down at the table and eat the rest of the cake. You made choice after choice after choice. In a similar way, 'I fell off my diet' deviously avoids responsibility for choices you've made.

□ **Feeling deprived** – *'I miss my biscuits.'*
If you believe you have no choice but to eat less, sooner or later you will feel deprived, full of self-pity and resentment. This can lead to apathy and depression and it can also create symptoms of stress. (1)

If you're more of a rebel you'll feel anger, irritability or an exaggerated addictive desire to eat: intense cravings and obsession with food. However, if you are particularly good at being compliant you can feel entirely positive and successful for a while. Eventually, though, compliance wears thin, rebellion returns, and you start overeating again. (2)

Whenever you feel deprived of food there is sure to be some form of prohibitive thinking involved: rules, restrictions and threats. When you change the way you are thinking, when you take responsibility by reminding yourself of your own choices, these feelings will subside.

Here's an example. For our first few sessions, one client experienced an intense addictive hunger every time she came to see me. When we talked about it, she realised that she had expected me to somehow make her or tell her to stop overeating. The stirrings of rebellion against this were automatic. After we had established that as far as I was concerned she was free to eat as much as she wanted to, the hunger disappeared.

☐ **Treats and rewards** – *'I deserve it.'*
Everybody knows forbidden fruits are the sweetest – but usually it's not fruit that gets forbidden, it's fat, salt and refined products. If you think of any food as forbidden, whenever you don't eat it you'll feel deprived, which will seem like you're being punished. So eating it will feel like a freedom and a reward, at least while you're actually eating.

If we could somehow think of celery as forbidden, we'd consider it a treat, because we always want all the more whatever it is we think we can't, mustn't or shouldn't have. We do this because we need to know we are free. One of the worst things that can happen to us is to have our freedom taken away, so it's not surprising that we don't like restriction and instinctively rebel against it. It's this deep, instinctive attraction to something that's forbidden that adds power to our addictive desire.

The key is free choice, but in fully acknowledging this, do keep in mind the consequences of your choices, the complete picture of what it is you are actually choosing. Some choices enhance your health, others will be detrimental to it. *Instead of thinking of food as either 'allowed' or 'forbidden', think in terms of choices you make either to enhance your health or to impair it.*

☐ **Strong compulsions to overeat** – *'I couldn't stop myself.'*
These could result from a situation where you became particularly upset about your weight. Perhaps some clothes you tried on didn't fit, or your doctor gave you a warning, or somebody made an insensitive remark about how thin and attractive you once were. Your automatic reaction is one of: 'I *have to* lose weight!' and 'I *have to* stop eating so much!' You might at first go into a state of compliance and cut back on your addictive eating, or go straight into rebellion. Either way, you set yourself up for some serious compulsive overeating sooner or later.

Another – extreme – example is eating food that's gone bad. It's mouldy, rotten and maybe already in the rubbish bin, but the overeater who habitually takes little responsibility will feel strongly compelled to eat it, simply because it's so very much 'not allowed'. People who take so little responsibility often become stuck in a permanent state of rebellion: 'I'm not allowed to eat *anything*, so I'm going to eat *everything*, just to prove I'm free to do so.'

Many of us enact a version of this, eating things mainly because we think of them as forbidden and because we want to confirm to ourselves that we are free to eat them. We may not be aware that this is our motivation at the time, perhaps explaining our behaviour by telling ourselves: 'I just can't resist them.' When I've eaten like that I've often (but not always) thought to myself that I don't really enjoy what I'm eating as much as I thought I would. My desire was more to assert my freedom of choice than a desire for the taste or texture of the 'forbidden' food.

☐ **Rebellious reaction to dietary advice** – *'I don't like vegetables.'* One example of this is my pork-pie story earlier in this chapter. A friend of mine provided another. Ellen had asked me to explain the principles contained in a book I was reading about nutrition, and I told her that an example of a recommended meal would be about 170 grams (6 oz) of lean protein with green vegetables. My friend's instant reaction was: 'Well, that just makes me want to eat chocolate!'

I'm not suggesting that you act on advice without question, simply that you consider the sense of it for yourself – and watch out for the spontaneous rebellion that occurs whenever you think that someone else might tell you to eat less.

☐ **Strong dislike of natural hunger** – *'I can't stand being hungry.'* At the beginning of this chapter I asked you to imagine what it would feel like if you were locked up in a cell and given only just enough food to survive. Part of an entirely appropriate reaction to that situation would be anger and resentment, which would probably be stronger whenever you felt genuinely hungry. Therefore, lack of responsibility brings about a negative response to hunger, because it feels as if you are not freely choosing it.

☐ **Justifications** – *'I couldn't live without my cheese.'*
If you are very attached to the reasons you give yourself as to why you eat addictively, it's probably because you tend to deny your freedom of choice. The justifications provide you with some sort of permission to overeat.

In order to be convincing the justification must fit the circumstance: a holiday abroad, a family gathering or an evening alone can all seem equally compelling reasons to overeat. Justifications can also be found in any number of physical or emotional upsets.

Perhaps you can see that if you were locked up in that cell you might well conjure up an illness in order to be released. In real life ill health isn't deliberately chosen. It can be quite automatic and unconscious, taking the form of a stomach upset or headache, and can seem to be a very sensible reason to eat something. Justifications are tricky because they can often look perfectly reasonable.

When you do begin to take more responsibility by reminding yourself you always have free choices, you will see that you don't need to justify eating anything. You can just do it. It's your choice. Then you can begin to let go of some of the justifications.

☐ **Passivity** – *'I have no willpower.'*
Feeling hopeless, resigning yourself to the way things are, wishing someone would come along and solve the problem for you or looking for magic cures are all good indications you are not taking responsibility yourself.

Looking for a magic pill is not going to help you. It will only serve to discourage you once you find that the instant cure you are looking for doesn't exist. When you take control of your overeating it comes as the result of the choices you and only you can make, not as a result of some gimmick that supposedly relieves you of that responsibility.

A crucial step in taking responsibility is accepting that nobody else can or should do this for you. *Not only can nobody else do this for you, but you already possess all the magic you need to get this job done.*

☐ **Believing it's impossible** – *'I would eat less, but I can't.'*
'Why Don't You, Yes But' is one of the games in the book
Games People Play by Eric Berne. There are two players, one
trying to help while the other skilfully avoids taking
responsibility, and begins with the latter describing a
problem they have. For example:

A   I live on my own and I cook such huge amounts, I always
     eat way too much.
B   Why don't you just make smaller amounts?
A   Well, I love to make minestrone soup for example, and
     there are so many ingredients I always end up with a
     great big potful.
B   Why don't you freeze some of it, in separate containers?
A   It doesn't freeze well, it loses its flavour.
B   Why don't you keep it in the refrigerator and have it over
     a few days?
A   Yes, I try to do that sometimes but I find I eat it all in one
     evening. When it's there, it's so good I just want to keep
     eating it until it's finished.
B   Why don't you make minestrone only when you've got
     people coming over who can share it with you?
A   I just do a main course when I have company, like a pasta
     dish. I wouldn't want to make minestrone as well – I'd be
     spending all day in the kitchen!

This game is usually played out between two people, which
is one reason I advise you not to discuss with your family
and friends anything you define as a 'problem' you have
with eating. You're likely to end up playing the game! If it
seems as if someone else is trying to take responsibility for
your addictive eating, they might be welcomed initially
(compliance) but ultimately resisted and resented (rebellion).
You might find yourself playing 'Why Don't You, Yes But' with
me as you read through this book. I may make a suggestion,
and you automatically react with a 'yes, but' objection to it. In
fact, as I reread chapters I've already written, I sometimes react
with an 'yes, but' objection myself. Yes, I can be irresponsible
too! I'd like someone to come along and take care of all my

problems for me. For a long time I wanted someone to come along and write this book for me. I put off writing it for years because it seemed so difficult I wouldn't take responsibility for doing it myself. But finally, I took responsibility for writing it and you have the result of that in your hands. Taking responsibility produces results. If the minestrone-maker took responsibility, she would find her own solution.

And that's precisely where the growing up takes place: when we acknowledge our problems and recognise that we are the source of the solutions, particularly when it comes to eating, because that can be so completely within our control.

□ **Way of life** – *'I don't have the time.'*
Avoiding taking responsibility is, of course, a way of life which extends far beyond eating issues. Especially common among overeaters are those people who take on far too much responsibility for others, behaviour which is sometimes referred to as 'relationship addiction'. They are the obsessive care-takers and rescuers whose lives revolve around trying to sort out other people's problems. *They take responsibility for everyone but themselves.*

Low self-esteem drives this way of life: it's another attempt to gain self-worth through pleasing others or fixing things for them. People who live like this may appear to be saints and martyrs, but they renege on their responsibilities to themselves, and so lose out on true self-esteem.

They may justify their lack of responsibility by telling themselves: 'I would look after myself more, but I'm so pre-occupied with looking after him/her/them, I can't possibly cope with it all – if only they would sort out their lives, I'd be able to sort myself out.'

If you recognise yourself in this, it will be important for you to make changes here too, in order to get into the habit of taking more responsibility for yourself. Simply refuse to rescue others by refusing to assume responsibility for them. Allow them to be who they are and to make their own mistakes. By detaching yourself in this way, you will be inviting them to take responsibility for themselves – which is really all they need to do.

I'm not suggesting you should stop caring about them. In fact, allowing others to take responsibility for themselves is the most caring thing you can do for them. What I'm suggesting is that you stop trying to make other people do what you think they should do. Stop trying to control others, and you will free yourself up to take control of yourself. (3)

By the way, if you see yourself in these words, notice whether you're reading this book mostly with other people in mind. It's very likely that much of it will seem to apply to people you know, but you could be ignoring its relevance to *you* because you are thinking in terms of what other people need to learn. For example, Susan, an overweight friend of mine who read the manuscript of this book, did nothing about her own eating, but started to give advice to friends and family about theirs. The advice, need I say, was not appreciated.

By all means let people know about this book if you think they may benefit from reading it, but if you talk about it I strongly advise you to be cautious about what you say.

Willpower and How to Use Yours

Willpower is quite literally the power of your will, and the most important thing to understand about your will is that it is *free*. Your will is in your power to freely choose what you will and what you will not do. When you deny your freedom of choice you deny your free will. *And you can't possibly use your will effectively while you deny it.*

This is how you undermine your willpower. When someone says: 'I have no willpower' it's the same as saying: 'I'm not taking responsibility for my choices.'

The solution is in your acknowledgment of choice. The most common error is to consider the consequences of a certain choice and then to conclude that you have no choice. So watch out for ways of thinking along these lines:

- 'If I want to lose weight, *I have to* stop eating so much.'

- 'If I want to stay in control of my eating, *I can't* eat any more ice cream.'

- 'If I take responsibility for my eating, *I won't be able* to eat everything I want.'

This is *false reasoning*. You can want something sincerely, even desperately, but this never removes your free choice in the matter. The only circumstances in which you wouldn't have completely free choices about your eating decisions would be if you were locked up in that cell. You wouldn't be overeating, but it wouldn't be your choice. You wouldn't be responsible. Whenever you notice this way of thinking, correct it to thoughts such as these:

- 'Yes, I do want to lose weight, but I could continue to overeat and put on even more.'

- 'I do want to stay in control of my eating, but I still have the option of eating addictively.'

- 'Taking responsibility means knowing I am able to eat anything and everything I want.'

I'm not suggesting you go ahead and eat everything you want! And I'm not suggesting that you make a point of consuming your favourite 'forbidden fruits'. What I'm saying is, if you remind yourself you can eat anything you want, you will be able to make a choice. You need to know you have a choice before you can make one.

You might resist acknowledging choice because you then blame yourself and feel guilty for choices you've made in the past. Perhaps you take being responsible to mean: 'It's all my fault.' But blaming yourself is not the same as taking responsibility; it's judging yourself.

Taking responsibility means independent thought and independent decision making. You take responsibility when you recognise that you are the one who determines what you do, that your actions are up to you and nobody else. You take responsibility for your health by acknowledging that your physical well-being is up to you and nobody else.

Which choices are going to support our health and which will undermine it may not always be clear, and it's inevitable

OLD WAY OF THINKING

'I'm free to eat' ⟶ eating something

'I can't / mustn't eat' ⟶ not eating something*

*I realise this doesn't always work, but at least you try not
to eat something this way.

NEW WAY OF THINKING

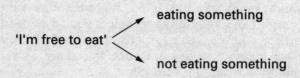

- Giving yourself permission to overeat may seem at first to be a dangerous thing to do. You may well be thinking 'Of course I'm free to overeat – I do it often!' and fear that reinforcing this message will make you overeat even more.

- This fear is understandable if in the past the only way you've managed to eat less is by telling yourself you 'can't' or 'aren't allowed' to eat something or 'have to' eat something else. The problem with this, though, is that when you think this way you set yourself up for a tough time while 'in control' and rebellion later.

- If you want to eat less, you are much more likely to succeed in the long term if you freely choose to do so. This means recognising that you could spend your entire life overeating, eating all the food you want, any food you like, any time, any place. Different choices lead to different consequences, but even actions that lead to severely impaired health and self-esteem *do not remove your freedom of choice.*

- By acknowledging free choice you gain the ability to eat less – without feeling deprived and without becoming rebellious.

that we'll get it wrong sometimes. We have so much choice when it comes to food! We are confronted with decisions throughout the day about what to eat and when to eat it, what is good for us and what is harmful, how much of it to eat, and whether or not it really is what we want at that time.

So often, however, we abdicate. We go with our own traditions or follow what everyone else is doing. Time and again we simply adopt the choices that others have made: our family, our peers, our culture, the food industry. Taking responsibility means gaining some knowledge of the facts, and then examining and challenging the assumptions we're making about what we're eating.

Taking responsibility is a process of growing up. When we were infants we were not responsible for what we ate. Taking more responsibility is a long process which begins when we first put food into our own mouths. Then we begin to make our own choices about what we will and will not eat, and eventually learn to shop and cook for ourselves or go out to restaurants and order our own meals.

As infants we demanded instant gratification; the ability to delay gratification is something we learn to do as we mature. Maybe you don't want to be grown-up, but what's nice is to have the ability to be either child-like or adult, as we choose. (4)

Taking more responsibility isn't a decision you make once and that's it. It's not a permanent state. But with practice, as you develop the habit of recreating it over and over, it becomes easier and more natural. The important step is to begin. You will start to feel better immediately.

You'll know when you're taking more responsibility because you will be able to make changes in your eating and feel good about those changes. You'll feel more powerful and more hopeful that you've got something which will last.

You'll know you're doing it when you don't feel deprived after you choose not to eat something. This is why taking responsibility is essential in taking control of addiction. It's very difficult to stay motivated if it feels as if you are depriving yourself.

You'll also know when you're taking more responsibility because you will experience less guilt and higher self-esteem. This is why self-esteem is a more effective motivation than losing weight. You may lose weight while you are 'locked up' in a diet, but if you are not taking responsibility – owning your own choices – your self-esteem may not improve.

No matter what happens, you are going to be thinking about food, on and off, for the rest of your life. You'll have thoughts about food every day, at many times throughout the day. You don't have a choice about that! What you do have a choice about is the quality of those thoughts. If you begin to think in ways that cultivate a more responsible relationship with food, the benefits to you will become obvious.

This isn't an easy, magic solution, but genuine self-esteem is your reward, and my hope for you is that you discover just how exciting that can be. In the next chapter we'll look at what choices you might make and how to go about putting choice into practice.

In other words   SANDRA

I was anorexic for only a short time before developing a compulsive eating and bingeing problem which I now recognise as rebelling against being inside a box of prohibitions against certain food in certain amounts.

After several successful years of psychotherapy, I resolved most of the emotional issues I linked with food and eating. But to my disappointment I still suffered from addictive behaviour, including compulsive eating, overeating, compulsive exercise and eating too little. I believed that discipline was the answer: eat enough, but not too much.

But trying harder was fruitless until I accepted freedom and responsibility. It wasn't more rules I needed. It was the knowledge that I was free to eat when and what I wanted: free to starve myself; free to exercise or not; free to binge. Only when I accepted that I was free to take any of these actions could I take responsibility for my choices.

Now, when I'm presented with a choice about food or exercise, I remind myself that I am free to do anything. Then, I ask myself what I want to do. Sometimes I get it wrong, but fine-tuning is part of living.

TAKING CONTROL

• If you often have cravings for a certain food, it's probably because you consider it 'illegal', and may have done so for a long time. Tell yourself before, during and after eating it: 'I'm allowed to eat this' and 'I can eat as much of this as I want, any time.' Give yourself permission, over and over again, to eat anything and everything you want.

I realise that you may fear giving yourself this freedom because you think you will then go ahead and eat anything and everything you want – and you may actually behave like this sometimes to begin with because at first you may recognise choice only superficially. You may continue to eat these foods, even though they may not be very good for you, because you are dealing with long-term, deep-seated beliefs, and they won't go away in an instant. I do want to encourage you to continue with this, though, because you will only be able to take genuine control of your eating when you have trained yourself to think in terms of the free choices you are making.

• Say to yourself: 'I can eat anything I want' every time you think about eating something. When you are in a restaurant, let yourself know you can have anything on the menu. When you are shopping for food, tell yourself you can choose to buy anything in the shop. Remind yourself: 'This is my choice' every time you eat, *especially* if you regard it as addictive or 'fattening'.

It may be true that you can't have everything exactly the way you want it. You can't keep eating everything you want without it affecting your health and self-esteem. But even though you don't have a choice about which consequences follow from certain actions, you still have free choices about which actions you take.

• Keep your addictive thoughts and the decisions you make about them to yourself. As far as possible, avoid discussing why you are or are not eating something. If anybody makes a comment about what you are eating, just don't get involved in a conversation about it.

• Possibly the most powerful denial of choice is created by the belief that you 'have to' lose weight (or 'can't' put on any more) and your attachment to this belief may be so strong that it alone causes your feelings of deprivation.

You may want to lose weight, but this is quite different from not having freedom of choice in the matter. The only time you would have to lose weight (i.e. you would have no choice) is if you were locked up in a cell and given very little food. While you believe you have to lose weight, you create a state of mind as if you were locked up and so create overwhelming states of deprivation and rebellion.

If it's difficult for you to understand that you don't have to lose weight, try this written exercise:

> Write down as many endings as you can to the sentence: 'I have to lose weight because . . .' leaving one line blank in between each ending. This identifies the thinking behind your false belief. Then go back over what you have written and in each blank line write the true statement. For example:
>
> I have to lose weight because I can't get into my clothes. (*false*)
> I could put on even more weight and go out and buy clothes in larger sizes. (*true*)

I'm not encouraging you to put on weight, I'm encouraging you to see that you have choices, so you won't feel deprived whenever you don't eat something. Then you will begin to move out of the compliance/rebellion cycle.

• Some people create feelings of deprivation, not because they believe 'I have to lose weight,' but because they believe

'I have to control my eating' or 'I have to eat less' or 'I have to stop overeating.' The 'I have to' and 'I can't' statements create the same problems described above, and the written exercise can be applied in the same way. Simply start your sentence with 'I have to stop overeating because . . .' (or words that fit best for you) and proceed in the same way.

• Write down six endings to: 'If I take 5 per cent more responsibility for my eating . . .'. Write down whatever comes to your mind. There are no 'right' answers. Here are some endings written by clients of mine:

. . . I won't eat the leftovers from my children's plates.
. . . I'll eat more vegetables.
. . . I'll eat less.
. . . I'll feel a lot better about myself.
. . . I'll feel more in control of my eating.
. . . I'll be a lot happier.

Notice that the first three lines refer to specific changes in behaviour and the second three are the benefits you feel from making those changes. Notice if your endings contain examples of both types. I suggest you do this exercise as often as you can; once a day would be good.

This exercise is an example of those contained in Dr. Branden's *The Six Pillars of Self-Esteem*.

References

1. Stanford University neuroscientist and stress expert Robert Sapolsky describes a number of experiments that show how stress increases when we have no choice – or even when we just think we have no choice.
    'This is an extraordinarily powerful variable in modulating the stress-response . . . the exercise of choice is not critical; rather it is the belief that you have it.'
    From *Why Zebras Don't Get Ulcers* (WH Freeman).
2. Of course, if you are in some kind of treatment programme, perhaps even hospitalised, this loss of personal responsibility is quite real:
    'Patients in our own clinic often comment on the security provided by the treatment, and data that we have collected during weight

loss programmes showed that craving and the sense of loss of control goes down and not up during the active phase of treatment.'

International Journal of Obesity (1996; 20, SI-S8).

However, this report goes on to say:

'. . . most weight control treatments induce weight cycles . . . a series of patients were reduced to normal weight in a hospital programme. By the four year follow-up almost 60% of the patients were close to their initial weight with over one third having exceeded it.'

3. An excellent book which deals in detail with this aspect of addictive behaviour is *Codependent No More: How to stop controlling others and start caring for yourself* by Melody Beattie (HarperCollins).

4. The value of delayed gratification is explored in *Emotional Intelligence* by Daniel Goleman, Ph.D. (Bloomsbury) in which the author states: 'There is perhaps no psychological skill more fundamental than resisting impulse.'

7 What to Do about Wanting More

When we make a choice about anything it makes sense for us to understand what it is we are choosing. We make better choices when we know more about the alternatives available. When it comes to making choices about an addiction, people often think rather simplistically in terms of: 'Shall I do it or shall I not do it?' When we think like this, we overlook a crucial factor in our decision making process. This is our addictive desire.

The addictive desire is the driving force behind any addictive behaviour. Whether someone smokes a cigarette or takes cocaine or overeats, what they are doing is satisfying their particular addictive desire. For example, a smoker has an addictive desire to smoke and so they light a cigarette to satisfy it. They satisfy it and they reinforce it at the same time. It's only satisfied temporarily, of course, and before long the smoker will feel another desire, and another cigarette will be smoked. All addictions work the same way: first the desire to do whatever it is you're addicted to, and then doing it, which reinforces the addiction, creating the next addictive desire, and so on.

As someone who overeats, you have been satisfying and reinforcing your addictive desire to eat, possibly every day, for many years. The only other reason there is to eat is a genuine need for nutrition, which is often (but not always) identified by the natural body signal of stomach hunger.

Many people never feel their natural hunger because they feed their addictive hunger before their natural hunger appears. The more extra weight a person carries, the less they eat because of genuine hunger. More often they eat to feed their addiction.

Now we get to the biggest and most common mistake people make when they want to control an addiction: *usually people try to take control of addictive behaviour by trying to avoid feeling their addictive desire*. They reason that if they don't feel it, they won't feed it, and so assume they will be in control. Most smokers throw away their cigarettes and avoid temptations such as pubs and friends who smoke.

In the same way, those people who know they eat addictively at home in the evenings may make plans to keep themselves extra busy – the cinema one night, tennis the next, work late another night – all in a determined effort to keep themselves from experiencing their addictive desire to eat.

This kind of strategy, in case you don't already know it from your own experience, is flawed. It's flawed because its success depends on you not having an addictive desire, and that can only be a temporary solution.

You might, for example, decide to stop eating chocolate and not have any interest in eating chocolate for a few days. You think you're doing well because you're sticking to your intention, but I'd like to suggest to you that you're not accomplishing as much as you could. As you may well be aware, as soon as your desire resurfaces and you are lusting after your favourite chocolate treat, you will eat it. This is because you never faced your addictive desire in the first place. Or you do experience your desire for chocolate, but you see this desire as nothing but negative – something to be feared, resented and, if at all possible, eliminated.

Unless you begin to deal with your addictive desire in a more positive way, it doesn't matter how well-intentioned you are or how long you have abstained. For periods of time it may look as though you're in control, but all that's happening is that you aren't experiencing a strong enough addictive desire, or maybe you feel no desire at all. Alternatively, you feel it but you're fighting it, so it's only a matter of time before you give in to it.

Whether you're making a New Year resolution not to eat chocolate, going on a diet or cutting out fried foods, the familiar scenario is to start but not to continue. You might explain this by saying it's because you don't have any willpower or that you're incapable of discipline. The real explanation is more likely to be that your addictive desire was initially avoided, and when it could no longer be avoided, you satisfied it.

How much chocolate or fried food you eat is not the point. The real question is: are you willing, ever, under any circumstances, to deal with your addictive desire to eat? As far as taking control of an addiction goes, the addictive desire is where the work is done and the changes are made.

You can't take control of an addiction by avoiding it or wishing it would go away. It's only when you come to terms with your addictive desire that things will really start to change. This way may not be so easy, especially to begin with, but the rewards are both profound and lasting.

Bringing Shades of Grey into Focus

Overeating is unlike other addictions in that you aren't going to stop eating entirely, whereas a smoker's goal, for example, would be to stop smoking altogether. The first step in dealing with your addictive desire to eat is to identify it. How can you be sure whether or not you are about to satisfy your addictive desire or your nutritional needs?

As we saw in Chapter Five, it's impossible to define addictive eating precisely; nobody will ever be able to say exactly where this addiction begins and ends. This doesn't mean it doesn't exist or that it can't be recognised and managed.

In fact, it's impossible to say *precisely* where a great many things begin and end – a mountain, the dawn or your ankle, to name a few examples. Nobody can say at which exact point your leg becomes your ankle and your ankle becomes your foot. This doesn't mean you don't have an ankle, that you can't use it or point to it and say: 'That's my ankle!'

In the same way, we can point to addictive eating and say in general terms that it's eating anything other than what your body needs to stay in good health. The problem with addiction, though, is that it's out to deceive you, because that's what an addiction does. Your addictive thinking will have you convinced your leg goes all the way to your toes if that will justify eating another slice of cake! What we need to do is find some way to know for sure. We need some kind of structure with boundaries that will be tougher to dispute.

The solution is contained in two very simple tools, called Times and Plans. First of all, I'll explain what I mean by these terms, then we'll take a look at how to use them to get control of your addictive eating.

☐ **Times**   The purpose of the 'Time' is to give you a way to choose to *start* eating which is least likely to be influenced by your addictive thinking.

This is how you use this tool. Whenever you finish eating, whether it's a meal or a snack, set a Time for yourself. Your goal is to get to that Time without eating anything. To begin with, I suggest you set a Time at least one hour ahead and no more than four hours ahead.

For example, if you finish your lunch at 1.30 pm, you might set a Time of 4.30 pm. Your goal is not eating anything at all until 4.30 pm. Then, when 4.30 comes, you don't have to eat at your Time. You have a choice, either to eat something and when you've finished set another Time, or to set another Time without having eaten anything.

By setting Times you will be able to gain a real sense of control over your eating. It may be difficult to know whether or not you are about to eat more than your body really needs, but you can be absolutely sure of whether or not it's 4.30!

☐ **Plans**   The purpose of the 'Plan' is to give you a way to choose when to *stop* eating which is least likely to be influenced by your addictive thinking.

This is how you use this tool. The idea is to decide what you intend to eat at a meal, just before you start eating, before you take the first bite. You decide how many portions, what size portions, how many courses, how many second helpings you plan to eat at that meal.

You don't need to weigh food or measure it too exactly, and you don't need to have it all in front of you to start with. The idea is to create, just before you begin to eat, a mental picture of what it will be; make it as accurate as you can. (You might begin a Plan days earlier when shopping for the week; the idea is to finalise the Plan at the point when you start the meal.)

You always have complete control over choosing what your Times and Plans will be. It makes sense to set a Time when you think you'll be ready to eat again, but you'll need to learn through trial and error how far apart to set the Times and how much you need to include in your Plan at each meal. Undereating can be just as much of a problem as overeating. As you practise this approach and gain more control over your eating, you will learn what Plans to make at each meal so you'll be ready for more food when your next meal is due.

After you have some experience with this, and on the days when it fits your schedule and your nutritional needs, you can set the Times further apart and/or make the Plans smaller – but this isn't the main purpose of using these tools. The real value in using Times and Plans is that you will be able to see your addiction more clearly. It's only when you see your addiction that you can get to work on taking control of it.

Sooner or later, you'll want to eat something before you get to your Time. And it's inevitable, when you get to the end of your Plan, that you'll want to eat some more. This is your addictive desire to eat. Believe it or not, this desire is your golden opportunity to make real and lasting changes in your relationship with food.

The point at which you take control of an addiction is when you are experiencing your addictive desire – at the very moment you want to eat addictively. In that instant you have a chance to open a door and walk through, and when you do you'll find that you have crossed a crucial barrier.

You'll be stepping out of your 'comfort zone', but you'll be gaining the ability to be in control of your addiction. Real control.

This may sound unrealistic. I know I'm suggesting something very new, and it's understandable if you're doubtful and hesitant at first. Just keep an open mind. Now, let's take a look at the addictive desire to eat and see what we can do about it.

Accepting Your Addictive Desire to Eat

Accepting your addictive desire to eat means being willing to feel it, without satisfying it, fighting it, resenting it or doing things to make it go away. Here are some ideas to help you gain this acceptance of addictive desire:

☐ **Understand it**   Your addictive desire is a thought that pops into your mind and says: *'Let's eat!'* Often, when it's strong enough, there's a sense of urgency to it, as if it has to be acted on immediately. But it can also start as a simple thought which gets satisfied hours later, after you've been to the shops, for example.

It happens because you get reminded by different things – places, people, thoughts, moods, stress, times of day, days of the week, routines, physical ailments – which you associate with eating.

Often a particular cue will trigger a desire to eat a particular thing. For example, years ago I got into the habit of buying a Kit-Kat every time I got on a train, so turning up at a station would automatically trigger a desire for one, even though I would never think of them any other time.

Most people can identify patterns to their addictive eating: what they tend to eat when they're alone at home, when they're upset, when it's four o'clock, when they go to the cinema. This eating has nothing to do with nutritional needs and everything to do with the conditioned response which is at the heart of all addictive behaviour.

THE ADDICTIVE DESIRE TO EAT

The scientist Pavlov found that dogs could be trained to expect food (they salivated) whenever a light flashed, simply because the light had flashed when they had been fed in the past. Below is a list of things which may trigger your desire to eat, by association, simply because you ate in response to them in the past.

Consider how often you have reinforced such connections. This is not intended to make you feel guilty, but to enable you to accept the fact that the connection won't magically disappear. It fades in time, when you no longer reinforce it, provided you are genuinely choosing to accept feeling it.

Places – shops, restaurants, your kitchen, your car, the cinema, the pub, your workplace, your parents' home

Circumstances – cooking, family gatherings, being offered food, travelling

Time of day – mid-morning, one o'clock, mid-afternoon, time to go to bed

Your senses – sight, smell and taste of food, advertising and product promotion

'Negative' emotions – boredom, sadness, grief, frustration, anger, self-pity, fear, anxiety, embarrassment, regret, loneliness, rejection

'Positive' emotions – enjoyment, happiness, celebration, relaxation, accomplishment, feelings of connection and intimacy

Physical sensations – aches and pains, changes in menstrual cycle, symptoms of stress, feeling tired, drop in blood sugar

Altered states of consciousness – being drunk or under the influence of 'recreational' drugs

- Often these associations are made unconsciously. You aren't aware of the cue or you aren't aware of your addictive desire to eat. You just want to eat something or you just find yourself eating. Times and Plans will help you gain awareness of your addictive desire to eat. It's not essential to identify each cue.

- You could experience two or more of these cues simultaneously, and even natural hunger as well. Use the tools of Times and Plans to determine when and how much to eat.

- Remember, it's your choice: either satisfy and reinforce your addictive desire, or accept the uncomfortable feeling of wanting to eat in return for some improvement in the quality of your life.

☐ **Identify it**   Sometimes the addictive desire can be so subtle you don't even notice it. It can be a simple, reasonable, everyday sort of thought, flickering through your mind, which suggests you eat something. If some food is on its way into your mouth, it's quite possible you are experiencing, and are about to satisfy and reinforce, your addictive desire to eat. Becoming aware of that is the first step to taking control.

At other times, though, your addictive desire will feel stronger, like a void that demands to be filled. You will feel quite uncomfortable if it's not satisfied. It may well feel like hunger, and it may be difficult for you to know whether it's an addictive desire or a genuine need for food.

So how can you be sure it is addictive? By using this technique you begin to learn how to identify and define your addictive eating. It's deceptively simple:

If it's before your Time or more than your Plan, there's a good chance it's addictive.

And if it's a desire for a Kit-Kat, it's addictive because you don't need it in order to stay in good health.

☐ **Choose to accept it**   The addictive desire wants to be satisfied. But just because you have an addictive desire to eat, you don't have to satisfy it. You have a choice. Remember: if you forget you have choices, the addictive desire will be exaggerated. It can be exaggerated in different ways:

– It can become more frequent, so you want to eat more often.

– It can become more intense, turning into a strong craving.

– It can last longer, as a persistent nagging.

For example, you might experience an intense addictive desire as soon as you set a Time because you assume you then can't eat anything until you get to that Time. You may even resist setting Times in the first place because it feels like you're putting yourself into the no-choice cell of deprivation.

It is draining to try to control your eating in a mental state of deprivation, so remember that every time you feel an addictive desire to eat, you always have a choice about whether to satisfy it. *You don't ever **have to** accept your* *addictive desire. If you remember this, you will be able to regard Times and Plans as tools to use rather than rules to obey.*

If you still don't fully understand this distinction, reread Chapter Six, working on the exercises at the end. If the concept about choice is new to you, it may take a while for it to become real to you. This doesn't mean it won't work eventually. It just means you need to be persistent. Keep reminding yourself that you can eat anything, any time, as much as you want. Then make the genuine, free choices you really do want to live with.

☐ **Feel it**   You may experience your addictive desire to eat physically, as a sensation in your body. But remember it's coming from your mind. This happens with all addictive desires. For example, research on addiction shows that abstaining cocaine addicts experience their addictive desire as a physical feeling. It can be brought on simply by watching a video of people taking cocaine. (1)

In the same way, you may have a desire to eat simply because you see or smell food or because you see other people eating. But food is different from other addictions. You don't need to watch someone else doing it because you will be doing it yourself at dinnertime! Simply eating a meal will often trigger the addictive desire. This is very common. You may begin a meal not all that interested in eating, but by the end of the meal your addictive desire is in full swing and you want to go on and on and on and on.

By accepting the desire you finish your meal while still wanting more. You bring out that addictive desire and choose to let yourself feel it. This is incredibly powerful, because you directly confront the addiction.

When you can get to the point where you simply let yourself experience those feelings of desire instead of feeding them, and without getting upset about them, then you are in a very powerful position of control. You are able to say: 'Yes, that second helping looks wonderful and I know I would enjoy eating it, but I'm choosing to accept this feeling of desire instead of satisfying it.' And you will be able to do that any time, with any food you desired. You won't be able to make this change in an instant, but try to move in that direction. Take it at your own speed.

☐ **Be aware of it**   Don't make the mistake of thinking that the goal is to eliminate desire. This may seem to happen for days or even weeks at a time, but often it just means it's been repressed.

Repression is an automatic coping mechanism we all have the power to employ. Automatic means it's not consciously chosen. For example, many people automatically repress feelings of anger. They were probably taught as children that the expression of anger was unacceptable, and so they learned to feel it as little as possible in order to stay 'in control'.

In the same way, your addictive desire to eat can be repressed for periods of time simply because you regard it as unacceptable. It's very likely that you learned to repress your addictive desire while you went on diets.

There's another way the addictive desire can disappear for a while. When people over-indulge their addiction, to food, alcohol, cocaine or whatever, the binge is inevitably followed by a 'crash' phase where there is no addictive desire at all. Aversive thoughts will predominate – guilt, together with nausea and physical discomfort – which override any desire for more. The desire returns in time, of course, when the crash phase has passed.

Many overeaters go through 'binge/fast' cycles in this way. The 'fast' phase of the cycle may seem to be your ideal state – but the absence of addictive desire doesn't mean you're in control of your addiction. It's the presence of the desire, not its absence, that gives you the opportunity to take control.

☐ **Value it**   If you really believe you are freely choosing to accept your desire, it's possible to see it as a positive experience – an opportunity. Focus on what you are gaining in self-control and self-esteem, not on what you are losing: a second slice of cake, for example. See it as a trade-off: 'I could eat the cake, but if I accept this desire I have for the cake I stay in control of my eating.' (This assumes the second slice of cake wasn't part of your Plan.)

By building a positive response to your addictive desire, you gradually diminish the power of your addiction to food. In fact, the strength of your addiction could be measured in terms of how much you don't want to feel your addictive desire to eat. Many people develop routines, such as shopping on Sundays or going to the cinema after work, which they do *mainly* to keep themselves out of the kitchen. They attempt to take control of their addictive eating by avoiding their addictive desire.

This is what leads you to be out of control in the first place. The addictive desire cannot be permanently avoided, and when you are not prepared to accept it, you are at the mercy of your addiction and its whims. You eat whenever you happen to have a desire to do so, and sometimes, because of circumstances you cannot avoid, you can end up eating all day long.

A binge is an unsuccessful attempt to satisfy an addictive desire. Your attempts to satisfy it keep it going, especially when it's fuelled by a persistent emotion such as anger or loneliness. As it's impossible to satisfy, the desire only abates when you become preoccupied with thoughts of self-loathing.

So one reason to accept and value the uncomfortable feeling of desire is because not accepting it is more uncomfortable in its own way. *Then you stop trying to satisfy something that is fundamentally unsatisfiable.*

☐ **Face it directly**   A diet/weight-loss way of thinking will lead you to substitute something 'innocent' in an attempt to satisfy your addictive desire. As a result, you end up consuming enormous quantities of things such as sunflower seeds, lettuce or tea. Or you substitute a pot of low-fat yoghurt for a high-fat, high-sugar dessert at the end of a meal.

I knew a weight-loss group leader who would eat four heads of iceberg lettuce at once, with no dressing. Clearly she was feeding an addictive desire for something else, and clearly her motivation was not to gain weight.

When your motivation is to take control of your over-eating, you choose between feeding your addictive desire and accepting feeling it. Compromising, with cottage cheese, for example, helps you to avoid facing that choice, which means that the fundamental conflict is not resolved.

☐ **Resolve the conflict**   A state of conflict arises when you want two different things at once and you can't have both of them:

1. You want to stay in control of your addictive eating *and*
2. You experience your addictive desire to eat.

This is the essence of withdrawal from addiction: a conflict which often feels like a real battle. Wanting to avoid this conflict has contributed to your long-term failure to take control of your eating in the past. You need to go through the conflict in order to take genuine control. Making real change requires facing this difficult but unavoidable challenge.

The battle will become easier in time. Addictive eating reinforces addictive eating, because whenever you feed an addictive desire you strengthen it. When you choose to accept the desire you diminish it. The way to weaken your addiction is to be willing to accept feeling your addictive desire. Then you resolve the conflict, not by avoiding the desire but by accepting it.

☐ **Accept it**   The less you fight and resent feeling your addictive desire, the more quickly you resolve the conflict it presents. Simply allow yourself to feel it, because it's your resistance to it that makes it more persistent.

Some people deal with their emotions in the same way. Many people, perhaps as a result of personal development training or therapy, believe in the principle of letting themselves feel their feelings. They think positively about having 'negative' feelings, whatever they are. They accept that these difficult emotions are part of life and that to face them is more beneficial to them than trying to avoid and ignore them. For similar reasons, it is beneficial to face and accept your addictive desire to eat. (2)

☐ **Do it for yourself**   Being in a state of desire and conflict is difficult and uncomfortable. If you attempt to do this in order to gain approval from others you are likely to feel martyred, and this is likely to backfire on you. Remember from Chapter Three that wanting to lose weight is a motivation that is primarily about what others think of you.

You will not succeed if you try to resolve the conflict in order to please or impress others by 'looking good'. It's your *private experience* of higher self-esteem and improved health and vitality that leaves you feeling as though you've gained something when you choose to accept feeling your addictive desire, instead of feeling like you're missing out on something.

☐ **Laugh at it**   Whenever you feel your addictive desire to eat, your first reaction may be to blame yourself, perhaps judging yourself as greedy, indulgent or worse. Accepting your desire also means accepting yourself for having the desire, realising that the only reason you're feeling it is that you ate addictively in the past – it isn't because you are fundamentally flawed.

Forgiving yourself for the overeating you've done in the past is essential, and a sense of humour about it and about yourself will help you a great deal.

Applying Times and Plans

Don't underestimate the value of Times and Plans. The technique's effectiveness lies in its simplicity. It's flexible from day to day, adaptable to your unique needs and, most important, self-determined. It's a very powerful technique – but only if you use and value it. It will work very well for you if you use it in a rigorous way. If you use it half-heartedly you will get half-hearted results.

Here are some of the finer details about putting this technique into practice:

☐ **Drinking**   There's no need to set Times and make Plans for drinking liquids. Be aware, though, that you may be trying to satisfy your addictive desire to eat by drinking, whether it's juice, wine, tea or water.

☐ **Watching the clock** If you find yourself frequently checking to see if it's your Time yet, this is your addictive desire working. It is more effective if you make a deliberate choice to accept the desire, reminding yourself why you are doing this, rather than impatiently waiting for your Time.

☐ **Forgetting to set a Time or setting one and then forgetting what it is** Set yourself a Time as soon as you realise you don't have one. Make sure it's at least one hour after you last ate. It's best if it's a somewhat challenging space of time ahead. If you keep forgetting your Times, you could write them down.

☐ **Going past the Time without realising** Either eat or set a new Time.

☐ **You don't know when your food will arrive, so you aren't sure when to set the Time** For example, you know you'll want to eat when you get home, but you don't know exactly when that will be. Or you're at a restaurant or someone else's house for a meal.

It's fine, to set a Time of, say, 6 pm or 'whenever I get home', so long as you then don't start to rearrange your schedule to arrive home earlier! The same applies to food that's being prepared for you by someone else.

☐ **Setting the same Times every day** It's OK to have some standard Times, for example, always to eat lunch at 1 pm. For many people this is necessary. However, it's better to consider your nutritional needs as much as possible, instead of keeping to a routine just because it is a routine.

☐ **Eating while cooking** When cooking for yourself, you could include the cooking in your Time and Plan, and eat some food while preparing it. It's after your Time and in your Plan, so there's no problem. Otherwise, be aware of whether you're tasting something to see if it's cooked and seasoned properly or whether you're swallowing mouthfuls in an addictive way.

One of the liberating things about this technique is that you don't have to worry about whether you're eating too fast, or eating while you're standing up, travelling, talking, reading or watching TV.

☐ **Starting a meal while you feel strong addictive hunger** Your addictive desire could continue for some time, especially if it's tied up with a persistent mood, and this is another value in using Times and Plans. There will be some days when you feel an addictive desire to eat on and off all day, but if you stick to Times and Plans – because you do need to eat sometimes – you'll know you're in control.

☐ **Setting Times and Plans, sticking to them, but still feeling like you've eaten too much** Estimating exactly how much you need to eat will always be guesswork. However, you can do this in a controlled way by using the techniques. Just remember for next time. It's perfectly normal to eat more on some days, and less on others.

☐ **Eating from a buffet or shared bowl** Make your Plan by selecting what and how much you are going to eat and putting it on your own plate or napkin. If you want to include a second helping in your Plan, be clear about what that's going to be before you take the first bite.

☐ **Eating before your Time** A genuine concern for your health, such as feeling shaky or having a hypoglycemic attack, is a valid reason to eat before you get to your Time. Otherwise, unplanned eating is addictive eating.

I Never Deny Myself!

A client told me this recently with a look in her eyes that said: 'and don't you dare suggest that I should do so!' She was telling me that if she has a strong desire to eat something, she has every intention of satisfying that desire, and she has every right to do so. She *does* have every right to do so, and I'm not going to tell her what choices to make. But she will have to live with the consequences of consistently following that course of action, consequences she was not happy with, which was why she was seeing me in the first place.

At first glance, accepting a strong addictive desire to eat may sound like a fate worse than death. But consider the possibilities. When you accept your addictive desire, instead of thinking it shouldn't be there or trying to make it go away, a lot of things fall into place. To achieve this, you will need to struggle through some real conflict. Otherwise you will just skim over the surface of the problem.

The biggest mistake people make is trying to find an easy solution which eliminates their desire. Taking control of addictive behaviour is always difficult. It's not impossible, but it requires some effort. It's easier if you accept that it *does* require effort. Avoiding that truth makes it worse, because as soon as it gets difficult you are incapable of dealing with it. You set yourself up for failure simply because you are not willing to face the difficulty.

You can continue to resist and resent the difficulty of controlling your eating. Or you can see that this is an inevitable part of the process and regard the difficulty as the sign you are beginning to take control.

There may be days when you feel your addictive hunger on and off all day long. The more you have, the better, because that's when you practice dealing with your problem. *The decisions that are the toughest to make are where you will make the most progress.*

All this will take time, so be patient with yourself. Keep at it, and there will come a time when you become much more willing to accept your addictive desire to eat. Regard every obstacle as an opportunity. In most cases, overeating is a long-established pattern of behaviour, and it takes a lot of careful thought to turn it around. However, in time, as you continue to use these techniques, your addictive desire will be less and less of a problem.

Experience your compulsion to overeat and make your peace with it. It's a sign that you are not overeating, but keeping your word to yourself. It's the way you apply the brakes. You need no longer be afraid of situations which you associate with addictive eating. You can create, in the words of another client of mine, a relationship with food that is 'a source of contentment and even euphoria, rather than an abiding sorrow'.

After all these words about desire, I do want to make the point that at times in the past you must have made choices to accept feeling your addictive desire to eat, even though you could have satisfied it. This chapter is to encourage you to do that more deliberately, more powerfully and more consistently.

For some people, though, physical conditions make this process more difficult. This is what we'll look at next.

In other words   ANNETTE

When I used to diet, I was often able to push the thought of food away. But I knew it would always come back, and it always did. And I was unprepared. Now, when the desire to eat more than I need comes up (and it still comes up!) I take it as an opportunity to discover what it is that I really want.

Now, the desire to eat is no longer the monster that was always lurking in the background. I am able to recognise it, take a look, and try to establish contact. It's still there, but I know it so much better, much better than I ever thought I would. Sometimes we are fighting each other, but I don't feel helpless any more.

When faced with a chocolate cake, I would desire it intensely. It was almost like being in love. At the same time, I knew I shouldn't eat it. So I ate it and felt bad. Now, I still sometimes eat it, though most often I don't. But now it is no longer the one I love. It's just a chocolate cake.

The way to get through your addiction is not by denying it or trying to avoid it (which you can't anyway) but by experiencing it. This is a very important and exciting process which gave me access to a lot of information about myself, over and above the eating problem.

I can change. I can decide. I can take charge. I eat food, food doesn't eat me. I don't feel guilty about my desire. I feel it but I don't feed it.

TAKING CONTROL

• Since your addictive desire to eat is a product of your mind, it can only be dealt with by your mind. In a nutshell, this is how to deal with your addictive desire to eat:

THE OUTLINE

I have a desire to eat.
I have the freedom to eat.

Either:
I choose to eat addictively.

Or:
I choose to accept my desire to eat in order
to gain the benefits of staying in control.

• When was the last time you had a strong addictive desire to eat which you didn't satisfy, even though you could have?

• Notice how you benefit from using Times and Plans and the Outline. Make some notes about this. It's very likely you will take these benefits for granted later on and it will be helpful to have as much written down as you can, especially about the benefits that have nothing to do with weight loss.

• If you tend to overeat late in the evening, as many people do, you can make use of these techniques to take control and work toward eating earlier. It's much better for your health to have your food digested before you go to bed.

• Availability makes any addictive desire stronger, so if you surround yourself with the food you love, you are likely to experience a more persistent desire. Don't drive yourself crazy with this; find a balance. It's fine if there are some things you prefer not to keep at home.

• Keep all this to yourself. Take full responsibility for what you are doing by telling no one of your Times and Plans. If you don't bring up the subject, you won't invite other people's involvement.

This obviously applies to your day-to-day life, not to group meetings, counselling or therapy sessions you attend to talk through issues surrounding overeating. There's a big difference between discussing the Eating Less technique with the help of a counsellor or group, and bringing it into daily conversations with family or friends.

References

1. From *The New Scientist*, October 1, 1994:
   'These cues are very powerful – videos of drug paraphernalia cause changes in brain chemistry and skin temperature in addicts. And they are also very hard to avoid.'
2. In *The Six Pillars of Self-Esteem*, Nathaniel Branden writes about the value and practice of acceptance:
   'When we fight a block it grows stronger. When we acknowledge, experience and accept it, it begins to melt because its continued existence requires opposition.

   'To "accept" is more than simply to "acknowledge" or "admit". It is to experience, stand in the presence of, contemplate the reality of, absorb into my consciousness. I need to open myself to and fully experience unwanted emotions, not just perfunctorily recognise them.

   'Accepting does not necessarily mean liking, enjoying or condoning. Acceptance of what is, is the precondition of change. And denial of what is leaves me stuck in it.'

8 No More False Hunger

In this chapter we make a brief diversion from addictive thinking to look at false hunger, a physical problem some people encounter that can make it hard for them to eat less. Some people never feel false hunger, and some only start to feel it after they have cut down the amounts they eat. Their overeating was masking the problem, and eating more appropriate amounts of food brings the problem of false hunger to the surface.

There are two causes of false hunger:

1. Stomach acidity Often misinterpreted as natural hunger, stomach acidity can be quite painful, so very understandably it makes it difficult for you to keep yourself from eating. Even the possibility of feeling hungry later on can drive you to overeat rather than risk feeling the pain of an empty acid stomach. I struggled with stomach acidity for some time, so I know what I'm talking about. I overate a lot in an attempt to get rid of the pain.

Of course there are many kinds of antacid medication, but it's not a good idea to use them for a long time. It's much better to learn what's causing the problem in the first place. Eating healthier food has proved to be the most effective solution for me, together with regular exercise and very occasionally a session of acupuncture.

As far as healthy eating goes, nutritionists advise us to balance twenty per cent acid-forming foods – meat, poultry, fish, eggs, grains and cheese – with eighty per cent alkaline-forming foods – most vegetables and fruits. Over-acidity can lead to serious problems such as ulcers and arthritis, so it's important to deal with it, quite apart from the issue of eating less. (1)

2. Low blood glucose   A second cause of false hunger is the sudden rise and crash of blood sugar levels caused by eating carbohydrates that release insulin and glucose into the bloodstream too rapidly. This connection between carbohydrates and insulin/glucose release is rated by the glycemic index (GI).

High GI foods (those that carry a high glycemic index rating) trigger an undesirably high insulin/glucose response. Low GI foods cause insulin/glucose to be released at a slower rate, providing the body with a steady stream of energy and sustained mental alertness.

Foods with a high glycemic index have a place in a healthy diet. The problem is that many of us have eaten too many of them too often. Simply eat less of the high GI foods, and when you do, *eat them together with protein* and low GI foods, to balance out the effects. Foods should not be regarded either as healthy or unhealthy judging by their glycemic index rating alone. It's just one factor of many, and certainly fat content should also be taken into consideration.

As well as creating false hunger, eating too many high GI carbohydrates is associated with many problems, including: low blood sugar (hypoglycemia, mood swings, headaches, dizziness), late-onset diabetes (hyperglycemia; it accounts for more than 90 per cent of diabetics), fatigue, high blood pressure, heart disease – and difficulty losing excess body fat. (2)

Well-modulated insulin and glucose levels result in a reduction in body fat, no false hunger, increased and sustained energy, enhanced mental alertness, reduced high blood pressure and cholesterol, greater cardiovascular fitness and less reliance on artificial stimulants such as caffeine and nicotine.

If false hunger is a problem for you and you take measures to eliminate it, it will leave you with your addictive desire to eat to contend with. This desire is much easier to deal with when you aren't experiencing false hunger as well.

THE GLYCEMIC INDEX OF CARBOHYDRATES*

Insulin is released quickly by:

Grain-based foods
most breakfast cereals:
cornflakes, muesli, shredded
wheat, quick-cooking porridge
oats, puffed rice, puffed wheat
white and brown bread
white and brown rice, millet
cous cous, taco shells, pitta
bread, rye and wheat crackers,
pastry, croissants, cakes,
muffins, waffles

Sugars
table sugar, glucose, maltose,
honey

Vegetables and fruits
cooked parsnips, beetroot,
corn, broad beans,
potatoes (especially baked,
instant, chips, microwave)
raisins, dates, figs, prunes,
banana, mango, papaya,
watermelon, pineapple
canned apricots, fruit cocktail

Snacks and drinks
popcorn, corn chips, puffed
rice cakes, biscuits, shortbread
Mars bars, Lucozade, Fanta

Insulin is released moderately by:

Grain-based foods
white and whole-wheat
spaghetti and pasta,
whole-grain wheat bread,
bulgur wheat, brown basmati
rice, Kellogg's Special K and
All Bran

Sugars
lactose, sucrose

Dairy products
low-fat ice cream

Vegetables and fruits
peas, baked beans, carrots
(cooked), sweet potato,
oranges, kiwifruit

Snacks and drinks
most chocolate bars,
potato chips,
orange juice

Insulin is released gradually by:

Grain-based foods
whole-grain rye bread
oats (whole, slow-cooking)
barley

Sugars
fructose

Dairy products
ice cream,
yoghurt,
milk (whole and skimmed)

Vegetables and fruits
most green vegetables
soya beans, kidney beans, lima
beans, lentils, black-eyed peas,
chickpeas, tomato soup
cherries, plums, pears, grapes,
peaches, grapefruit, apples,
apple sauce, dried apricots

Snacks and drinks
pure chocolate
peanuts
apple juice (unsweetened)

* For reference see: *American Journal of Clinical Nutrition* Vol 62 (1995), pages 8715–8895.

Even so, you are likely to come up with a host of reasons why you should feed your addictive desire, and this is the subject of the next two chapters.

In other words   **FRANCES**

The Times exercise focused me in on what and when I was eating and how food affected my health and energy. I had always believed my eating was fairly healthy, but that I ate too much. However, I soon began to realise that I was not able to last between meals and reach my Time goals, as I would become shaky, tired and unable to concentrate. Previously I had been eating more often, unaware that it was not the quantity of food that would help me last between meals, but whether it was low GI food.

This was most noticeable during the mornings. Once I had changed my breakfast to include low GI food, I no longer ran out of energy mid-morning but was able to keep going without overeating.

This has created a radical shift in my eating patterns and my energy levels. It has also allowed me to focus more on my day rather than constantly thinking about the next meal.

TAKING CONTROL

• I've kept this chapter short because these subjects are well covered in other books. If you want to learn more, I recommend reading:

The Zone by Barry Sears (HarperCollins), which discusses in great detail the problems associated with elevated blood glucose levels. A simplified version, which includes recipes, is his later book, *The Zone Diet*.

Gut Reaction by Gudrun Jonsson (Vermilion) is an excellent book on digestion in general.

References

1. 'All joint problems, such as arthritis, are produced by acidity in the body. This acidity can be caused by high intakes of antibiotics or sugar, or incompletely digested food. . . . Rheumatism, too, has acidity at its root, as do frozen shoulder, tennis elbow, lumbago or back pain.'
   From *Gut Reaction* by Gudrun Jonsson (Vermilion).
2. During World War II, underweight soldiers suffering battle fatigue were given insulin injections in hospital to make them gain weight. This worked very well, except that sometimes it induced a coma, so the practice was stopped.

9 Your Reasons Why

Whenever we feel an addictive desire to eat, simultaneously we'll come up with a reason to satisfy it. The reason may flash through our minds faster than lightning. It justifies our decision to eat: 'I'm going to go ahead and eat this because . . .' We may eat because we'll enjoy it or because it will comfort us when we feel miserable. We want to join in with others or because we feel bored. Or perhaps we tell ourselves: '. . . I'd better finish it off before it goes bad.'

The addictive desire always wants to be satisfied, and our addicted minds will automatically select the most plausible reasons available at the time.

To take control of addictive eating, our aim is to become aware of the reasons we are using. They tend to lurk at the back of our minds, not completely recognised. They encourage our addictive eating but when they are not identified they cannot be brought out into the open for examination.

On examination, some of your reasons could be sound. Others may contain kernels of truth but be of questionable value. Others again may serve no purpose at all other than to insist you satisfy your addictive desire.

Call them reasons, justifications, explanations or excuses. You use them to justify *how much* you are about to eat, *how often* you eat and the *quality* of what you eat. You don't need to judge these reasons as 'right' or 'wrong'. Some could be appropriate in some circumstances but not in others.

If you eat more food than your body needs, you are too attached to too many of these reasons and use them too often. *Instead of creating the results you want, you live with the reasons why you couldn't manage to succeed.*

Determine which reasons serve you and which block your way. Only when you are aware of your reasons for eating can you freely choose. Then choose which reasons you want to use, and aim to use them within the structure of Times and Plans.

It's essential to have some reason to justify eating! An anorexic may not accept any at all, even the risk of dying of malnutrition. But you don't *have to* eat in response to your reasons. It's always your choice whether or not to satisfy any desire to eat, addictive or not. Identify your desires as addictive or non-addictive by using Times and Plans. Then develop the habit of listening for the reason you are giving yourself for satisfying an addictive desire.

There are probably an infinite number of justifications for eating, limited only by your addicted mind's imagination, which is vast. Below are some typical reasons and suggestions about how to let go of them.

Typical Justifications for Addictive Eating

☐ **Habit and tradition** – *'I always eat cornflakes for breakfast,' 'I always eat popcorn at the cinema,' 'I always eat chips at this restaurant,' 'It's the way I was brought up,' 'I'm Italian so I eat pasta,' 'If it was good enough for my mother it's good enough for me,' 'We always eat pizza on Thursdays,' 'My husband has to have his fish and chips,' 'I always finish a meal with something sweet,' 'It's lunchtime.'*

It is possible to eat according to your traditions within the structure of Times and Plans. It's also possible to recognise and accept the addictive desire which is triggered by a particular circumstance or time of day. Habit plays a significant role in any addiction. It's not the complete explanation for addiction, but it's a part of the picture. People who stop smoking experience their addictive desire in exactly the same way. For example, they feel their desire to smoke at exactly 5.30 as they leave their office, if it was their habit to smoke then.

To take control of your addictive eating, you don't need to change the routines with which it is associated. That will be impossible in some cases anyway. For example, you may buy chocolate bars at the corner shop on your way home. Unless you move to the North Pole you won't be able to avoid corner shops. Just expect to feel your addictive desire in those circumstances, especially at first. It will help to use the Outline.

By the way, notice that you are just as likely to justify feeding your addictive desire by something which is out of your normal routine, such as a holiday, an unusual excursion or visit from a friend.

☐ **Stress** – *'I always eat when I'm stressed,' 'I've had such a hard day at work,' 'I need to relax.'*
Although created mainly in the mind, stress is, at least in part, a genuine physical problem so it's tempting to seek a physical remedy in overeating. However, far from alleviating the problem, addictive eating actually makes you more susceptible to the physical symptoms of stress. This is because both stress and addictive eating impair your immune system. Not only that, but when you are stressed your digestive system is less efficient, so during stressful times it's wiser to eat lighter and more simple meals. Exercise, relaxation techniques such as yoga, meditation and autogenic training, and cutting out stimulants such as caffeine and sugar are effective antidotes to stress.

This is where you can really see addiction at work, because the chances are you will not want to regard these as viable alternatives. Your addicted mind latches on to the best reason to snack on biscuits and coffee, not the best reason for a visit to the gym! The difference between your level of interest in genuine solutions versus overeating could be seen as a measure of your addiction to food.

Remember, it's always your choice: feed and reinforce your addiction or acknowledge the addictive desire to eat triggered by symptoms of stress – and devise new strategies that really work. (1)

☐ **Physical well-being** – *'I don't feel too well,' 'I have a headache,' 'I'm cold.'*
Any physical ailment, upset, ache or pain can be a cue for an addictive desire, simply because in the past you have

conditioned yourself to eat in response to such things. This does not necessarily mean that eating would be an appropriate response. All it may mean is that you are experiencing your addictive desire again.

'I'm constipated.' The best cure is not eating more but exercise and plenty of water – and avoiding the processed foods that create the problem in the first place. If you tend to suffer from constipation, notice which foods you have been eating, and learn by trial and error. Also, there are very good natural remedies, such as aloe vera juice and linseeds, available from healthfood shops.

'I have PMS.' There is a connection between the food you eat and premenstrual syndrome. Several books and articles have been written on this subject. (2) You can choose food which alleviates the problem and eat it in a controlled way. This is quite different from feeding the addictive desire frequently associated with these times of the month.

'I'm tired and need a pick-me-up.' This could be a very important reason to eat something – or it could be one of your favourite excuses for overeating. The way to tell the difference is to see whether you really do get more energy from eating, and this can only be learned by trial and error. If you feel dizzy or tired, and then perk up when you eat, this may indicate you have been undereating. Either it's been way too long since you ate something, or what you last ate was of poor nutritional quality. (This is assuming you don't perk yourself up with artificial stimulants such as caffeine, sugar or chocolate.)

If you sincerely suspect you have undereaten, eat something immediately. This is a valid reason to eat before your Time.

☐ **Natural hunger** – *'I'm starving,' 'I'm really hungry,' 'I might get hungry later on.'*
A feeling of emptiness in your stomach, natural hunger is one of the best reasons to eat, although it's not a reliable signal for everyone. Sometimes I eat when I'm naturally

hungry and sometimes I don't. The important thing is that I don't fear it.

Your body isn't harmed by feeling hungry sometimes. It's only your addicted mind that objects. Natural hunger doesn't necessarily mean you are undereating, and some amount of natural hunger is actually beneficial to you because it means your body isn't loaded down with food to digest. Digestion is one of the most demanding tasks your body performs, so natural hunger means your body is relaxing instead of being overworked and overloaded. Your body feels lighter and has more energy and vitality, and your mind is more alert. Because you're not overeating, your self-esteem is higher, too.

Natural hunger should be a pleasant and even enjoyable sensation which just comes and goes. There should be nothing uncomfortable about it. It may be hard to believe at first, but in time, as you work through your addictive thinking, you will actually enjoy feeling some natural hunger every day.

□ **Social** – *'Everybody is eating this and I want to join in,' 'Eating is a way to be social,' 'It would be rude not to accept it,' 'I'll eat a lot to show it's appreciated.'*
If getting other people's approval is the most important thing to you, you'll feel torn in two directions: compelled to join in and eat the same as others but, at the same time, concerned about whether you're looking slim enough. As you may already know, you can't possibly win!

Notice how often you let other people dictate the quality, quantity and frequency of your eating. At times it may be appropriate – but not always. It's essential for you to be able to say, at least sometimes: 'No, thanks' or 'Can I save it for later?' And it's important for you to be able to do that and feel OK about it. You can assert yourself in a polite and sensitive way, and other people may not be as offended as your addiction wants you to imagine.

Be aware, though, that others may, perhaps unconsciously, try to sabotage you. It's likely that the people around you eat addictively, and your addictive eating helps them to justify theirs. They may fear change in you, and not fully understand what's going on.

'I only have a good time if I'm overeating.' If you forget you are making choices and why you are making them you can feel miserable, envious and martyred when you are eating less than usual or less than everyone else. If you deal effectively with your addictive thinking you will enjoy staying in control of your eating. You will still enjoy the good company and the good food.

'I must eat it now while it's still available.' This is like saying: 'I'll eat it now while I still can, because I won't be able to later.' Instead, give yourself permission to eat it now and permission to eat it at any time in the future. If someone offers me something gorgeous, and I see eating it as addictive, it will help me to say no if I allow myself the possibility of eating some later. If I still want it, I can include it or something like it, in my next Plan.

☐ **Pleasure and satisfaction** – *'It looks so good I have to have some,' 'I enjoy my food,' 'Food is my hobby, my career and/or the love of my life,' 'I deserve it,' 'I won't feel satisfied unless I have more.'*
Remember that pleasure is an integral part of addiction. *The smoker, drug addict and alcoholic all pursue pleasure, and in doing so value it more highly than their health and self-esteem.* This is what you do too, when you eat addictively.

As an overeater, you confuse the appropriate pleasure and satisfaction everybody gets from eating with the satisfaction of your addictive desire. For example, you get to the end of a huge meal and think: 'Now I'm satisfied!' This appears to be a natural and reasonable response – and it is, in as much as you have satisfied your natural hunger. But your addictive appetite has also been satisfied, and this is probably what you are referring to.

The tools of Times and Plans will help you to distinguish between your natural and addictive appetites. When you use the Outline to make fewer and fewer choices to feed the addictive desire, you can derive enormous pleasure from eating in a guilt-free, controlled, non-addictive way. This is consistent with good health and high self-esteem.

☐ **Nutrition** – *'I haven't had enough protein/vitamin C/iron today,' 'I don't know much about nutrition, so I'd better eat a lot to make sure I get enough of what I need.'*
If you are that concerned about your health you have the best motivation there is to eat lower quantity and higher quality food. A substantial amount of research supports this. The way to improve your immune system, slow down the ageing process and live a longer and healthier life is to choose a wide variety of foods that are the highest possible nutritional value – and not eat too much. (3)

'I'm pregnant so I'm eating for two.' It's possible that pregnancy will throw your eating off balance for all sorts of reasons. Take your doctor's advice as to how rapid your weight gain should be. If you are gaining too much weight too fast, perhaps you have discovered a new justification for addictive eating.

☐ **Denial** – *'It's just a little tiny bit,' 'Just this once,' 'I eat less than my skinny friends,' 'I have a very healthy diet.'*
One of the most compelling reasons to overeat is to convince yourself that you are not overeating at all. This justification is common to all addictions, at some point. Smokers say: 'I don't smoke very much so it doesn't affect my health.' Alcoholics say: 'I never drink alone, so I can't possibly have a problem.' It's one of the most powerful ways for an addiction to justify itself.

Much of the research on obesity is complicated by the fact that people who overeat underestimate the amounts they have consumed. The overweight subjects are supposed to write down everything they eat in a day, but researchers discover the discrepancies when they compare these records with analyses of urine samples that show how many calories have in fact been consumed. It's entirely possible the subjects don't deliberately intend to mislead. They are simply in the habit of fooling themselves into believing they eat less and aren't even aware they are doing it. (4)

We can also delude ourselves into believing we eat the highest quality, healthiest diet, when in fact we don't. Very often we make a few token adjustments – buying semi-skimmed milk, for example – and use these to convince ourselves we eat wisely. Then we justify satisfying any addictive desire by saying: 'I normally eat such healthy food, a few biscuits won't make a difference.' Perhaps it won't – but do notice how frequently you use this justification to choose poor-quality food. There have been times when I've used it every day.

☐ **Waste** – *'It's wrong to throw away food when there are so many hungry people in the world,' 'Today is its "best by" date, so I'd better finish it off now,' 'I'll eat the leftovers, so they won't be wasted.'*
But surely one of the most tragic examples of wasted food is overeating! There are people starving in this world, but eating addictively is hardly a solution. Throwing food away can be a very constructive thing for you to do because it sends such a powerful message to your addiction: this is better off in the bin than in my stomach! It's only your addictive thinking that will tell you otherwise.

☐ *Convenience* – *'I don't have time to cook, so I'll get my meal at M&S/ the chip shop/ the Indian take-away,' 'I'm at the chip shop, so there's only fried foods to choose from.'*
Your choices about what you are going to eat are made at least in part at the shop when you decide what to buy, and even in choosing which shop to go to. The same applies to choosing a restaurant because you know what you're likely to eat at each particular place, be it Chinese food, McDonalds or the pizza place with the salad bar.

Notice whether you're justifying eating poor-quality food by telling yourself you have limited options at the burger bar or that you don't have time to do any better. It's likely you are playing the 'Why Don't You, Yes But' game. Good-quality food – fresh vegetables and fruit, for example – is available if you really do intend to find it.

☐ **Doing badly** – *'I've already blown it, so why not keep eating?'*
This response usually comes from years of dieting, which creates the cycle of compliance and rebellion described in

Chapter Six. You may find it difficult to regain control once you've given it up, but stopping at any point is always an improvement. Simply set a Time between one and four hours ahead. If feelings of deprivation and rebellion are common for you, study Chapter Six, working on the exercises at the end, especially the last two.

'I'm too busy to deal with this,' 'I've got so much to cope with in my life, I can't possibly think about dealing with my addiction as well.' Tell yourself the truth: your overeating takes up time, thought and energy too. Making choices to accept your feeling of desire doesn't take a great deal of time, and among your rewards will be greater alertness and feeling more on top of things in general.

☐ **Doing well** – *'I've lost some weight, so it's OK to eat a bit more.'*
This justification contributes to yo-yo dieting. If losing weight is your priority (perhaps the only reason you accept your addictive desire), your motivation disappears along with the weight. So the more attached you are to weight loss, the more likely you are to put the weight back on! When you care less about your body size and shape, and more about the benefits you gain from higher self-esteem, especially from caring about your health as a preventative measure, staying in control of your eating will continue to motivate you.

'I've been to the gym and burned off 268 calories so I can eat a Mars bar and still be ahead.' Counting calories means that weight loss is still your main motivation. Counting calories has nothing to do with taking control of addictive eating. Counting calories is not necessarily related to weight, either, because this also depends on what kind of food the calories come from.

'I've been so good I deserve it.' What you may really be saying is: *'I'm doing so well, I'd better screw it up.'* If you have low self-esteem, success at anything will tend to feel unnatural, and you may get drawn into sabotaging yourself just so you feel 'your normal self' again. This is why it's so important to work on raising your self-esteem along with taking control of

your eating. *It's crucial that you esteem yourself enough to be able to tolerate your success.*

'I might become anorexic.' Anorexia and bulimia are characterised by low self-esteem, a strong fear of weight gain, wildly out-of-control bingeing and starving, and an obsession with food and dieting. Some of you may identify with these, but not as a result of reading this book and using Times, Plans and the Outline. Long-term overeaters could not develop anorexia or bulimia simply as a result of learning how to take more responsibility by dealing with their addictive desire to eat.

When you apply the Eating Less technique, the amounts you end up eating may seem alarmingly small, but only in comparison to what you used to eat. The truth is we don't need very much food in order to stay in good health, provided the food is of high quality. (5)

☐ **False self-identity** – *'I am an overeater, therefore I overeat,' 'I'm hopeless,' 'I have no willpower.'*
We all create false beliefs about ourselves – usually based on only one or two experiences at first – and then act in accordance with those beliefs over and over again, thus 'proving' their validity. When it comes to eating, it will help you to separate such beliefs from the truth.

For example, it may be true when you say: 'I eat addictively at times,' but when you make this mean something else – 'I have no willpower' – you are not being truthful. The truth here is more likely to be: 'Right now I'm not using my willpower to take control of my addictive eating.' Addictive behaviour is always supported by lies. Telling the truth is always the way to take control.

Watch out especially for all those ways you describe yourself as inadequate. *Your biggest obstacle to taking control of your eating could be your lack of belief in your ability to do it.* This is usually rooted in convictions such as: 'I'm too old, fat, lazy, weak, self-indulgent, busy and/or stupid.'

Underlying beliefs like these don't disappear in an instant, but it really will help you to remember that nothing about life is ever static. Change will happen slowly, even imperceptibly. The first time you refuse to use your negative beliefs as a justification for overeating you probably won't experience anything like a life-enhancing transformation, but if you continue to do that, in time, that's exactly what you'll achieve!

☐ **Past hurts** – *'I overeat because of my unhappy childhood/ my parents' divorce/ my divorce.'*
Painful experiences in the past, an unhappy childhood or even a less-than-perfect childhood, often provide a constantly available justification for any addiction you choose. Many addicts blame their past, claiming it's the reason they are the way they are today.

Alcoholics Anonymous tackles this issue by directing attention, not to the past injustice, which of course can never be changed, but to the alcoholic's continued resentment of the people involved. Begin to let go of your resentment, they advise, and you begin to heal yourself. Alcoholics who stay sober through AA don't need to approve of past hurts, just to forgive, and – a crucial factor in this process – to refuse to use whatever happened as a justification for drinking.

After all, it's not what happened in your life that creates the problem, it's the fact that you use what happened to justify overeating. You have your explanation about why you overeat and you tell it to yourself over and over again: 'This and this and this happened to me in the past and that's why I'm eating again.' What matters is not the past, but how you are justifying your overeating now.

'Addictive overeating represses emotions,' 'Whenever I try to diet I feel irritable and depressed,' 'I can't cope if I'm not overeating.'
When people take control of their overeating, they often become more in touch with their feelings, both joyful and painful. However, when you try to eat less in a mental state of deprivation, it's common to experience more extreme negative moods, especially irritability, self-pity and depression. This can lead you to conclude that overeating is the only way to achieve a happy life and acceptable personality. But these

negative emotions are not repressed feelings coming to the surface, but reactions to the denial of choice.

If you identify with this, increase your sense of free choice, and the bad moods will evaporate. Then you will discover that there is no monster lurking beneath the surface of your consciousness. You will simply feel more alive and more in touch with feelings of joy and enthusiasm as well as appropriate feelings of sadness and anger.

☐ **Present upsets** – *'I'm feeling sad and if I eat something I'll feel better,' 'Food is love,' 'Food is a friend who comforts me,' 'I'm bored.'*
It is also common to use current emotional states to justify addictive eating. Again, you are relating to food in the same way a drinker relates to alcohol, trying to use food as a way of coping with the difficulties in your life.

Notice, though, that overeating doesn't really help you cope with your life. If anything, it makes life harder for you.

It makes life more difficult because consuming too much processed and refined food contributes to poor nutrition. Not providing your body with the nutrition it needs is often an underlying cause of depression, stress and low energy. Research has shown that people who improve their nutritional intake feel stronger emotionally. (6)

Overeating also makes things worse because it creates a tendency to identify emotions as a desire to eat and nothing else. This inevitably results in some degree of emotional dishonesty, for example, when you pretend you're happy when really you're angry. In choosing to accept your addictive hunger you choose to sober up, you become more in touch with your true feelings and therefore more authentic. (7)

Whenever you feel upset and want to eat, you could spend some time simply allowing yourself to feel your feelings, asking yourself what you can learn from or do about this particular situation. It's that immediate, urgent addictive desire which is triggered by your feelings that's the most beneficial to accept.

Also, notice just how miserable you need to feel in order to use feeling bad as a reason to eat. Is it simply the ups and downs of daily life? It's not that eating won't or shouldn't cheer you up sometimes, it's just that this justification can easily become an excuse for any eating at all. It's one thing to feel comforted by a bowl of good soup when you're tired and hungry, but quite another to eat junk food all morning because you woke up a bit grumpy.

This doesn't mean your feelings are not important. But addictive eating is not the answer. The real solutions are not addictive, so tend not to hold the same appeal. Therapy, or a good recovery or personal development programme need cost no more than the amount of time and money you are currently spending on food you don't need. For many people, seeking help in this way will be an important part of taking control of overeating.

Many people explain addictive eating entirely in terms of covering up negative emotions. But remember, our addicted minds automatically select the most plausible justification available, so a happy moment of success and celebration can become an equally compelling excuse to eat addictively.

If our behaviour was guided by our wanting to avoid feelings and nothing else, going for a run would do just as well. But most of us don't even think of physical exercise when we feel upset. I'm not suggesting it as a solution; my point is that whenever you feel strong emotions, two things are happening: your feelings *and* your addictive desire to eat.

Addiction isn't just about avoiding unpleasant and unwanted feelings. It's also a strong attraction to particular sensory stimulations: the feeling of smoke in a smoker's throat or the creamy sensation of chocolate in the mouth. Through repetition, a deep groove is worn in our minds to satisfy our desire for that sensation – and any relevant excuse will suffice.

If you happen to be on your own, the justification may be loneliness, but if you're with friends it will be politeness or peer pressure. If you've got too much to do it will be to ease stress, but if you're bored, you tell yourself you're eating to fill the time.

☐ **If only** – *'If only I had a different job, if only I had a man/woman in my life, if only I lived in my own flat, if only my family were less demanding, if only I had a different man/woman in my life, if only my life was more interesting, if only I lived in a different country . . . then I'd be able to take control of my addictive eating.'*

Regrets or disappointments are often used to justify addictions. When you think about something you regret, it's likely you'll feel your addictive desire to eat, through association, because you ate addictively in response to those thoughts in the past.

If you want a reason to keep overeating, you'll always be able to find one. Alternatively, you could take responsibility for one thing you *can* be completely responsible for: what and how much you eat. Then, as a direct result you will be able to view the other circumstances in your life in a new way.

Once you take responsibility for overeating, you will begin to take responsibility for other things too. Although many of these things may depend at least partly on other people's actions – which you are not responsible for – you will be able to see more clearly what choices you have. And you will be motivated by higher self-esteem to take the actions that are required. But even if nothing else changes in your life, at least you will be in control of your overeating, and that's no small thing.

If your 'if only' justification has anything to do with not having enough money, remember what happened to Ernie Bailey. He won £11 million on the Lottery and barely stopped eating, drinking and smoking until he died of a heart attack twenty months later weighing 140 kilos (22 stone). (8)

Addictions often persist, despite the circumstances. You'll probably want to eat addictively when you're lonely *and* when you're surrounded by friends. When you're living your normal everyday life *and* when you're away on holiday.

Taking control of addiction, despite the circumstances, is powerful and liberating – and could well be the only really effective strategy you can take.

Follow Your Routines

Try not to make any other changes – keeping extra busy, avoiding certain people or places – in order to take control of your addictive eating. You can only break the hold of your justifications while in the relevant circumstances.

For example, if you eat addictively whenever you're bored, you have developed an association between addictive eating and boredom. So it's fair to assume that the next time you feel bored you'll want to eat.

Allow yourself to feel bored just as you normally would. If you face and deal with your desire to eat and don't try to fill the time in any other way, you work on resolving the conflict presented by the addiction. Then you are working through the problem by changing your priorities. You can only do this at the time it's happening, in those boring moments while you feel your desire to eat. You won't be able to think yourself through it ahead of time, only when you're there.

In those circumstances which provide you with your best excuses, you will make the most progress.

Many excuses, of course, are unavoidable anyway, especially those provided by our bodies. This is what we'll look at next.

In other words   **MARGHERITA**

Treating eating as an addiction was a difficult concept to grasp at first – after all, you have to eat a certain amount to live. But once you learn to recognise the addictive desire as separate from 'normal' eating, so many things fall into place.

All those excuses and justifications you've used for years fall away, and the simple acceptance that I EAT TOO MUCH is wonderfully liberating.

I now look at things like ice cream and chocolates and think 'I can eat that if I want to'. But now I am thinking about what I eat and getting into the habit of choosing the longer-term good of my body and self-esteem over the short-term moment of pleasure in the mouth – and it's a great feeling.

The technique of Times and Plans is especially useful for the evening meal, I find, as it keeps me from nibbling before and after dinner, when I'm preparing or clearing up. Instead of puddings, I now have a piece of fruit half-way between dinner and bedtime, and really look forward to it.

TAKING CONTROL

• If you call your overeating 'comfort eating' start to think of it as 'addictive eating'. Calling it comforting focuses on the perceived benefit only, which helps to justify it. It's more honest to call it addictive eating (which may also bring some sense of comfort). Satisfying any addictive desire will often – though not invariably – feel comforting, but the comfort is always at a cost.

• Awareness gives you power. Make a note, mental or written, of the justifications you use. If you listen for it, you'll hear the reason you give yourself just as you are making the decision to eat.

If you have difficulty figuring out what your justification is, just wait a while before eating until you know what it is. The longer you wait, the clearer your justification will become. Sometimes you might blank it out and go ahead and eat anyway. If this happens, discern the reason you gave yourself as soon as possible afterwards.

References

1. Patrick Holford has written an excellent guide to overcoming stress: *Beat Stress and Fatigue* (Piatkus).
2. The Women's Nutritional Advisory Service has been providing help for women for over a decade and has an eighty-five per cent success rate in reducing symptoms of PMS. Nutritionist Maryon Stewart, who set up the Service, has written a book called *No More PMS* (Vermilion).
3. See Reference 2, Chapter 5.
4. '. . . considerable inaccuracy in self-reports of energy intake has been documented. . . . Because the degree of underreporting

increases with intake, it is speculated that individuals tend to report intakes that are closer to perceived norms than to actual intake.'
Nutritional Reviews (1990; 48/10, 373–379).

'Whereas many people underreport their calorie intake, the degree of underreporting is greater in obese subjects.'
The New England Journal of Medicine (1992; 327, 1893–1898).

5. Dr Andrew Prentice of the Medical Research Council Dunn Nutrition Centre writes:
    '. . . energy balance only needs to be displaced by a tiny fraction for the cumulative effects to result in obesity. The fattest man in the world died recently in his mid-forties weighing 465kg (73 stone). Even this enormous accumulation of fat required an excess equivalent to only a small bar of chocolate each day. . . . human metabolism is very poorly adapted to recognise excess fat consumption and to reestablish fat balance.'
    British Medical Bulletin (1997; 53, 229–237)

6. 'In a survey conducted by the Institute for Optimum Nutrition, which involved giving people 'optimum nutrition achieved through dietary changes plus supplements', 79 per cent noticed an improvement in energy, 60 per cent had better memory and mental alertness, and 66 per cent felt more emotionally balanced.'
    From *Beat Stress and Fatigue* by Patrick Holford (Piatkus)
    'There are many nutritionally related causes of depression, the most common being sub-optimum nutrition resulting in poor mental and physical energy.'
    From *The Optimum Nutrition Bible.* by Patrick Holford.

    Also, Holford's book *Mental Health/Mental Illness: The Nutrition Connection* is well worth looking into on this subject.

7. According to Daniel Goleman in *Emotional Intelligence,* one of the most thorough studies of eating disorders, conducted with over nine hundred girls, identifies 'a failure to tell distressing feelings from one another and to control them' as a key factor. He goes on to say:
    'Some obese people are unable to tell the difference between being scared, angry, and hungry, and so lump all those feelings together as signifying hunger, which leads them to overeat whenever they feel upset.'

8. '£11M lotto hulk binges to death.'
    Reported in *The Sun,* (December 31, 1996).

10 'My Body Made Me Do It'

Often, people explain their overeating as being the result of some kind of physical imbalance, either a biochemical or nutritional deficiency. These justifications are all variations on similar themes, and they are all very common.

There is a biochemical side to any addiction, but now that scientists have more clearly identified what's going on, it has become popular to think of addiction purely in terms of biochemistry. This can be unhelpful. When we learn, for example, about how certain food enhances the mood-altering neurotransmitter serotonin, it's easy to feel hopeless about taking control when these magical and mysterious brain chemicals seem to be running the show.

☐ **Physical addiction** – *'I'm physically addicted to food,' 'My addictive desire is too much for me to cope with because it's a physical craving,' 'I can't help it,' 'I need it.'*
The food we eat has an effect on the chemical make-up of our bodies, and different foods affect us in different ways. For example, some food causes the release of extra hormones in the bloodstream, such as insulin and adrenaline, and the release of transmitters in the brain, such as serotonin and dopamine.

It is possible that the less you eat foods which upset the natural balance of your body, the less your body chemistry will cause you to want them. However, don't expect you will ever eliminate your addictive desire. It has a biological connection, but it is primarily a product of your mind.

You can test this yourself. Notice how, at least sometimes, you feel a strong addictive desire to eat something for no other reason than that it's become available. You walk past a certain shop, something enticing is offered to you unexpectedly, or you arrive home and remember the leftovers in the fridge. Notice how, at least sometimes, you feel satisfied only when you've eaten the last scrap of food on your plate, the last peanut in the bag or the last chocolate in the box – not the second to last. *It's your mind that has access to that information, not your body.*

Mandy, who attended one of my courses, is someone who used to believe that biochemical forces were behind her addiction to food. Half-way through the course it dawned on her that this didn't make sense. Her addictive eating was all done at the weekends. What she saw was that her body chemistry couldn't be affected by the days of the week.

Addiction to food means you've conditioned your *mind* to expect certain effects – good feelings of comfort, contentment and satisfaction – from eating addictively. Your addictive desire is inevitable because it lives on in your memory of having eaten addictively in those circumstances in the past. Time after time you said to yourself: 'Eat this and you'll feel better.' So you ate it and you felt better. You used your biochemistry to satisfy your addictive desire and to gain some sense of comfort or pleasure, and then you remember what happened and desire the same effects again. Your *mind* feels satisfied if the addictive desire is fed and your *mind* objects if it isn't. *The addicted mind uses the body as a vehicle, but the mind is in the driver's seat.*

So when you're standing in the supermarket loading your trolley with chocolate biscuits and ice cream, it's your mind making those decisions, not your body. It's only your mind that can take control of your behaviour by deliberately confronting the addictive desire.

You take control of addiction by choosing to feel your addictive desire, instead of trying to eliminate it. By doing so, you refuse to accept that you are the victim of your biochemistry. *It's not your biochemistry that controls you, it's your belief that biochemistry controls you that undermines your ability to take control.* (1)

If biochemistry really had the last word, how would anyone ever take control of an addiction without chemical intervention? Yet it's done all the time, every day, all over the world. Alcoholics stop drinking. Heavy smokers stop smoking. And overeaters cut back on their addictive eating. Many achieve long-term success, and the way it's done is by people sorting out their thinking, not their chemistry. For example, they identify sound motivation and start to deal with their problem in more conscious and responsible ways.

Smoking is widely thought of as a physical addiction, but I know from all the work I've done with smokers that the most intense and persistent cravings are *without exception* symptoms of deprivation, created by the denial of choice. With overeaters, feelings of deprivation result from an obsession with weight loss, years of dieting, prohibitive thinking and reduced levels of self-responsibility and self-esteem.

When you change your thinking and gain acceptance of your addictive desire, you overcome your fear of it and your resistance to it. It's then possible to enhance your mood when you want to by other means, such as exercise, meditation or supportive conversation. If you accept your addictive desire, they won't be displacement activities and therefore won't be a problem.

'I crave some foods because I'm allergic to them.' Another physical explanation for addictive eating, an allergy is the body's immune response to something it thinks is a potential threat. The most common food allergies are thought to be to dairy products and wheat. It could be that you are allergic to these or other kinds of food.

However, an explanation of allergy as a *cause* of addiction is insufficient as it doesn't explain why an allergy to cats, for example, produces an aversion, when an allergy to wheat is said to produce an attraction. The connection between allergy and addiction is more likely to be that addictive eating – overeating certain favourite foods over a long period of time – creates an allergic reaction, rather than the other way around.

Of course, once you know which foods you are allergic to, if you then think: 'Now I can't eat that any more' you can certainly end up with a more problematic attraction to that food. But that would be a result of the way you are thinking about it, the fact that you are denying choice, and not because of the biochemistry involved.

'*I have a sweet tooth.*' No, you haven't. You have an addictive desire for a drug known as refined sugar, which you call having a sweet tooth. The only connection this has with your teeth is that eating sugar causes tooth decay. This common justification provides a good insight into how insidious this addiction is, because so much in our culture makes it seem natural.

☐ **Body wisdom** – '*My body knows I need chocolate, bread, peanuts, bananas, etc.*'
Another popular reason for overeating, this justification claims a physical source without acknowledging addiction. For example, a friend of mine says that every so often she feels compelled to eat quite a lot of French bread. She explains this to me by saying there must be some nutrient in this bread that her body needs, and so she feels 'a need' for it.

You too may use this reason to justify either the quality or the quantity of what you eat – but do you ever use 'body wisdom' as a reason *not* to eat something? After all, if your body is that wise, why doesn't it stop you overeating? The reason it doesn't is that what you call your body's signal of nutritional need is more likely to be your addictive desire to eat, which is mental, not physical.

A client told me a similar story, with the same explanation, involving rice cakes instead of the French bread. Both French bread and rice cakes are extremely high GI foods. They cause insulin to be released into the bloodstream very rapidly, and so are more likely to be the kinds of food that people eat addictively.

This a theme I frequently encounter with my clients. Many of them talk about listening to their body as if they are deciphering messages about what they need to eat. Some books promote this idea too, suggesting, for example, that a desire for chocolate is your body's way of telling you that you need magnesium.

If this system really worked, no one would ever be deficient in any nutrients. As soon as people were low in iron or calcium or whatever, they would immediately crave the food they needed – spinach, for instance – and correct the problem. Perhaps people would even crave vitamin pills!

I'm not convinced that our bodies can send clear and reliable messages about what they need. If you are overweight or suffer from any diet-related illness, you evidently don't possess that intuition, or at least you are not in touch with it. Your body may know what it needs, but the message can only be received via your mind, and your mind thinks addictively. This means it will connive relentlessly to justify overeating.

Remember that people around you are probably overeaters to some degree too, so these facts will apply to them as well. Just because they believe, for example, that chocolate is valuable in some way doesn't necessarily make it true. (2)

Human beings survived for many thousands of years before chocolate was created. We don't need to fear the disease and famine which killed off our ancestors at an early age. We have our present-day epidemic of addiction to contend with.

One final point. There is an entirely different way you can listen to your body, and this is to observe physical states and sensations *after* having eaten. Are you lethargic and bloated or full of energy and vitality? These changes may be quite subtle, but keep noticing them and the foods associated with them. Pay attention to your body's excess weight, symptoms of ill health, headaches and low energy. Through them your body is clearly trying to tell you something important.

☐ **Justifying weight** – *'I was born fat,' 'It's just the way I am.'* Some people believe they just happen to be overweight, no matter what they do. This allows them to avoid facing the reality of their overeating, which means they are less likely to consider how much they eat every day, and how much sugar, flour, fat and salt they consume – the real cause of their problem.

'I have a low metabolism,' 'I put on weight if I just look at a piece of chocolate.' According to a great deal of research into this issue, slim and overweight volunteers, fed the same restricted diet, all lose weight in an entirely predictable way. When energy intake falls below energy requirements then – and only then – people lose weight. (3)

'My excess fat protects me from the world,' 'My weight keeps me from getting unwanted attention from the opposite sex.' Remember from Chapter Two that weight is an effect, not the cause, of your problem. Imagine someone trying to justify smoking by claiming some advantage to spending each morning coughing! Smokers have developed an addictive desire for cigarettes, not for coughing. As an overeater, you have developed an addictive desire for food, not for weight.

There are other ways to avoid unwanted attention from the opposite sex: wearing baggy, unfashionable clothing for example.

'It's middle-age spread.' There could be some truth in this, but just a little. Some experts say we can reasonably expect to gain about 2 kilos (5 lb) for each decade after the age of twenty – assuming we weren't overweight at twenty, in which case we could lose weight as we age. We need less and less food as we get older, so if we eat less, responding to our physical needs rather than our addiction, we will find that the all-too-common weight gain is not at all inevitable. (4)

'My mother was fat too, so it must be my genes.' Of course we inherit many features from our family gene pool, but we still have our own choices about how we live. For example, we don't have to hold the same political views as our parents, nor share their taste in clothes.

Our genes dictate what part of our body our weight goes on, but they do not control our eating choices and therefore do not have the final word about how much weight we will carry. (5)

Genes are often blamed for all addictive behaviours, but the same principle applies. *You may have been born with a genetic predisposition to become addicted, but you always have free choice as to whether or not you will continue to satisfy and reinforce your addiction.*

It's Your Choice

And so we return to the theme of taking responsibility for our actions. When we don't take full responsibility ourselves, something else must be held responsible instead. Whatever that thing is, we make ourselves its victims.

As victims we complain: 'It wasn't me – I didn't do it!' and explain: 'My body made me do it, my genes made me do it, my feelings made me do it, my mother made me do it, my father made me do it, my partner made me do it, my friends made me do it, my job made me do it, my addiction made me do it.'

In this way, instead of solving the problem, we perpetuate it. It's so easy to blame other people or our circumstances for our own reluctance to change, but the reality is that each one of us is responsible for whether or not we take control of our addictive eating. We are only victims if we allow ourselves to be.

Childhood experiences probably have an influence here. Many of us are trained to respond to the authority of others, rather than to respect our own. Perhaps you were not encouraged to take responsibility for yourself, to whatever degree was appropriate for your age. Maybe you were told what to do far too much and weren't allowed to make many choices you could have made for yourself. For example, you may never have been asked what you wanted to eat for your meals, you may have been forced to eat things you really didn't want, and you may have been taught to regard food as a reward or an emotional crutch.

Even though you may have been raised this way – and many of us were – it doesn't mean you can't learn to take responsibility now. Surely there are lots of things you've learned that your parents didn't teach you!

It's no use waiting for responsibility to appear, thinking that when it does you'll put it to good use. Things don't work that way. Your breakthrough can only occur when you see that nothing will change now unless you make it change. No one will simply show up in your life to solve this problem for you.

Make it your priority to take control of eating, rather than trying to control your weight. Then, make choices to accept your addictive desire to eat, using the tools of Times, Plans and the Outline.

For example, you get upset about something that happens in your life and so your first inclination is to eat something to distract you from feeling angry and hurt (even though you may know that eating won't keep you from feeling angry and hurt). If you then go ahead and eat, you reinforce your addictive desire – but now you know how to do things differently. Don't expect your addictive desire to disappear. Instead, be willing to feel it, and know that by doing this you begin to break your addiction.

Then you simply face the problem life is bringing you, which you cope with more or less efficiently whether or not you are overeating.

Gaining an acceptance of your desire gives you control over your addictive eating, and as a direct result you free yourself from the despair of having food run your life. In time the difficulty diminishes as you work through the conflict and you get better and better at identifying and dealing with your desire. You work on this every time you refuse to act on any of the reasons that justify your addictive eating.

In other words   JAVIER

Brought up in a family of overeaters, I had very high blood pressure and was very overweight. The doctor urged me to lose weight, but the mere idea of going on a diet made me feel hungry and eat more. This method gave me the insight to get my priorities right and to appreciate food for the beneficial effect it has on my health, both mentally and physically.

In the past I didn't give much thought to how I would end a meal and I would often end up gorging myself sick on bananas. Now, I remind myself that addiction thrives on confusion, so I make sure I have a very clear picture in my mind of what I need for optimum health, and by sticking to it I am keeping the addiction at bay. People comment on how much weight I've lost, but I know that the energy I've gained and my improved self-esteem are, by far, much more important than the lost fat.

TAKING CONTROL

• Write down as many endings as you can to the phrase: 'I overeat because . . .' Don't censor them, just write down anything that comes to mind, however far-fetched it may seem. Getting all your reasons written down where you can see them more clearly is a powerful step. Take a look at your list and choose which ones you really want to keep using and which ones you want to discard. You may discover a different range of reasons by trying variations on this exercise:

'I eat because . . .' 'I eat junk food because . . .' 'I eat addictively because . . .' 'I won't accept my addictive desire because . . .'

• It's not necessary to make other changes in your life and in your personality as part of this process. In fact, it's very liberating to establish for yourself that you can take control of your overeating and still be far from perfect – as we all are.

Taking control of eating doesn't automatically mean you will become more assertive, popular and clever, nor that you'll get a perfect marriage, exciting sex life or successful career. This may be disappointing, but it takes the pressure off, too!

References

1.   There is quite a bit of research which casts doubt on the notion that biochemistry causes addictive behaviour. For example, fifty subjects who suffered from 'binge eating disorder' were recruited for a trial and given a placebo for four weeks before they went on to the active medication that was being evaluated. Binge eating fell by an average of seventy-two per cent (from six to 1.7 binge episodes per week) during the placebo period. Twenty-two of the fifty became ineligible for the trial because they were no longer experiencing the required disorder.
International Journal of Obesity (1996:20, 1–6).

Similar results show up in research on other addictions which are commonly thought of as physical:
'Alcoholics were asked to indicate their desire for alcohol after drinking a drink containing one ounce of 100 proof vodka. The alcohol taste in the drink was disguised and only one-half of the subjects were informed that the drink contained alcohol. Only those subjects who were aware that they consumed alcohol reported significant cravings to drink further. Subjects who ingested the identical amount of alcohol, but who were not informed of its alcohol content reported no cravings. This demonstration, as well as others, indicates that craving depends as much upon one's cognitions as on one's physiological or pharmacological experiences.'
Appetite (1990; 15, 231–246).

In another experiment, a group of smokers were asked to refrain from smoking for twelve hours. On one day the group were given ordinary cigarettes to smoke and then gave detailed reports on how they felt. The procedure was repeated a week later, but this time they were given cigarettes which looked normal, but in which the nicotine – the active drug – had been removed:
'The regular and de-nicotinized cigarettes were equivalent in reducing acute withdrawal symptoms.'
Pharmacology, Biochemistry and Behaviour (1995; 50, 91–96).

2.   Dr Paul Rozin of the University of Pennsylvania isolated the active ingredient in chocolate – theobromine – and fed it to volunteers in the form of pills. The pills didn't satisfy their craving and Dr Rozin concluded:
'People like chocolate because it tastes good. It has nothing to do with the pharmacological effects.'
Reported in the *Daily Telegraph*, (February 14, 1998).

3.   Overweight volunteers who claim to be unable to lose weight, no matter what they eat, were studied at the Obesity Research Centre at Columbia University. The researchers concluded:

'The failure of some obese subjects to lose weight while eating a diet they report as low in calories is due to an energy intake substantially higher than reported and an overestimation of physical activity.'

The New England Journal of Medicine (1992; 327, 1893–1898).

4.   '. . . an average 70-year-old person needs 500 fewer calories per day to maintain his or her body weight than an average 25-year-old. The average 80-year-old needs 600 fewer calories. In short, from around age 20 onward, you need to take in about 100 calories per day less each decade to maintain the status quo.'

From *Biomarkers: The Ten Keys to Prolonging Vitality* by Drs Evans and Rosenberg (Simon & Schuster).

5.   'The increases in obesity seen in many Western countries over the past few decades, and the even larger increases in some of the Pacific Islanders whose countries have undergone dramatic lifestyle changes, are not reflections of genetic changes, but of gene expression facilitated by the environment. The most widely held view is that genes confer a susceptibility or predisposition to obesity and genetically predisposed individuals may be especially susceptible to aspects of lifestyle such as low activity and high fat diets, and gain weight more readily.'

International Journal of Obesity (1996; 20, S1–S8).

11 Addiction and Self-esteem

Now we have explored the three main aspects of psychological addiction, (responsibility in Chapter Six, addictive desire in Chapter Seven and justification in Chapters Nine and Ten), let's take a closer look at the relationship between addiction and self-esteem. To me, this is crucial because it's the exhilaration I feel when I have higher self-esteem *and nothing else* that keeps me going when the going gets tough. In fact, I think it only gets really tough at times when I've forgotten just how much my eating affects my self-esteem.

For self-esteem read happiness. It's what I feel when I wake up in the morning glad to be who I am, eager to tackle my day. It's easy to assume this depends on external circumstances – but have you noticed that your spirits can rise even though circumstances haven't changed in any significant way? Next time it happens, see if it could be the result of having recently behaved in a way that reinforced one of the 'six pillars' of your self-esteem, as described in Chapter Four. Maybe you asserted yourself in a new way, you took responsibility for something or you became more purposeful about getting something done. That's self-esteem in action.

When it comes to taking control of addictive eating, fully engaging with self-esteem as your motivation is a *major* change to make. It's entirely possible you haven't made this change yet, and losing weight is still the most important thing to you. This isn't surprising: our culture encourages this attitude, and it's likely you will be tempted down some false paths as a result.

One false path is substituting other behaviours. Often addictions themselves, these are likely to be things that don't contain many calories: cigarettes, chewing-gum, diet sodas, coffee, tea, alcohol, shopping, work and/or exercise. They may help you to keep your weight down, but they *don't* help you to control your addictive eating, and they *don't* support your genuine self-esteem. Any addictive behaviour will erode your self-esteem. Even more significant is your avoidance of your desire to eat, which means you don't take control of your overeating – you simply distract yourself or consume something else instead.

When weight loss is your goal, this kind of strategy makes sense, but you will never get to break your addiction to food this way. *There are many things you can do instead of eating, but if you are trying to control your eating through them, you will fail.* You will achieve only a partial, conditional acceptance of your addictive desire to eat and therefore gain only a partial, temporary success.

This is especially true of smoking as a way to control eating, because it usually becomes such an all-day, everyday part of your life. If you are a smoker, you will only be able to deal properly with your eating once you have stopped. If you are an ex-smoker, be aware that your desire to smoke may surface when you cut back on your addictive eating. If you gained weight when you stopped smoking, you substituted food for cigarettes. This means that your desire to smoke and your desire to eat will be interchangeable. (1)

By the way, caffeine, tobacco and alcohol can cause the stomach to become too acid and stomach acidity can be misinterpreted as hunger, as explained in Chapter Eight. If you intend to continue their use, take this into consideration and be especially careful to include plenty of alkaline-forming foods in your diet.

Another false path is in using appetite suppressants, which are drugs designed specifically to eliminate your addictive desire to eat, such as 'fen/phen', which was very popular in the United States a few years ago. The name comes from their composition: a combination of fenfluramine, which stimulates the production of serotonin in the brain but has the side-effect of making people very sleepy, and phentermine, an amphetamine-like drug which counteracts the sleepiness.

People who take these drugs lose interest in overeating because they feel satisfied with a lot less food. Their addictive desire has been taken away by the drug, and all that's left is a natural need for nutrition.

Although this may sound like the miracle cure we have all have been waiting for, this is far from the truth. 'Fen/phen' has now been withdrawn from the US market due to dangerous side-effects, especially damage to the heart. But the drug was officially approved, promoted as 'the most important weight-loss discovery of the century' and prescribed to thousands before its danger was recognised.

In addition, you only get the effect of these kinds of drug while you're taking them. As soon as you stop taking 'fen/phen', for example, serotonin levels fall and stay low for weeks, possibly longer, and it's possible the serotonin receptors become permanently damaged and never return to normal. (2)

A belief in pharmaceutical solutions, so prevalent in our culture today, is often a feature of an overeating problem because it's another way not to take responsibility. Any drug would need to be taken for life because there can never be a 'cure' for a behaviour such as overeating. Not only will they never work as instant 'cures', but remember that all prescription drugs have side-effects. Many of them are dangerous and some even fatal.

Using drugs is like going on a shopping spree with a credit card. You pay the bill later on but you still have to pay. Not only that, but when your addictive hunger does return you'll be less able to handle it because all the time you took the drugs you weren't exercising control of your addiction. You were just losing weight.

Oil and Water

It's difficult not to make improving your appearance your main priority. Just remind yourself that the real prize is the self-esteem you get when you take control of addictive eating. Losing weight is about wanting to make a superficial change in the way you look. Taking control of overeating profoundly changes your values and the way you live. The more you think in terms of fat and thin, the more you are missing the boat. *I want to suggest to you that you will not lose weight – and keep it off – until you don't care about it as much as you care about your health and your self-esteem.*

Like oil and water, these goals don't mix: either you set out to gain self-esteem or you set out to lose weight. For example, if you feel like eating before your Time, this doesn't necessarily directly affect your weight. You are unlikely to gain weight if you eat lunch at 12.45 instead of one o'clock. When you care about your self-esteem, you wait till one o'clock simply because you said you would. This strengthens the power of your word to yourself, which is really all you need.

Other examples can be found in the self-deceptions that surround an addiction. Perhaps you eat food you told yourself you were buying for others. Or you eat food all at once which you had intended to last a week. Or you kid yourself you ate a healthy meal because there was spinach flavouring in your pasta.

When your goal is self-esteem, you start out by telling the truth to yourself because that's what matters most to you. Eating the same amount according to Times and Plans won't directly help you to lose weight, but it will strengthen the value of your integrity with regard to food. Once that and the other 'six pillars' are in place, and especially when you have made taking responsibility for your health a priority, weight loss will follow, because you will have gained the ability to take control – and you will have experienced the motivation which will keep you on track.

You will never gain self-esteem from eating addictively because, by definition, it's bad for your health. It's possible you don't fully acknowledge the cost to your health because your addiction wants you to ignore this. And it's particularly easy to ignore because commercial interests in our culture encourage you to, and also because the effects on our health are usually so gradual.

Just as one cigarette doesn't give a smoker lung cancer, one biscuit won't make you diabetic, create a cancerous tumour or block your arteries. But smokers don't smoke just one cigarette and overeaters don't eat just one tiny scrap of fat or the occasional morsel of highly processed carbohydrates. When you eat addictively, an entirely appropriate drop in self-esteem lets you know you're doing something that is self-destructive instead of life-enhancing.

This is an essential survival mechanism, our own feedback system. It lets us know how we're doing. We can't get rid of it and we shouldn't even try. Self-destructive behaviour gets a minus in the feedback loop. It says: 'This thing you're doing is harmful to your health.' Or it says: 'You've betrayed yourself again.'

Unfortunately, people who tend to have low self-esteem often exaggerate this into a completely unreasonable: 'I don't deserve to live!' This is very unhelpful. Extreme guilt means you over-react to what you've done, which has the effect of invalidating the reasonable feedback. If you are abusing your body, it's appropriate to see this as wrong, but when your reaction is blown out of proportion by unreasonable guilt, feedback is often ignored and therefore not acted on. (3)

Many overeaters try to ease their guilt by hanging on to the addict's typical philosophy of life: 'Life is for living, so eat, drink and be merry – we're all going to die one day anyway.' It may be that you are fully committed to this view of life, but it could also be that when you really think about it, you aren't so sure. Perhaps you do think like this from time to time, but only when it's convenient, because it eases your guilt about your addictive eating.

Often people get 'wake-up calls' that cause them to question their 'Life is for living' philosophy. A wake-up call may arrive in the news that someone their age just had a stroke. Or they are diagnosed as diabetic or as having high blood pressure. Or they get cancer or something that might be cancer. Then many, although by no means all, will drop the 'Life is for living' philosophy and realise that life is for *living!* They start to make big changes in the way they eat, discovering willpower they never knew they had.

So why not pay closer attention to the wake-up calls and be more willing to act on them before they get too loud? It's only your addiction that's likely to object. You can find your very own, personal wake-up calls in symptoms of ill health you may have, and in your own experience of lower self-esteem.

Acting the Part

High self-esteem isn't a luxury, it's a necessity. When it's missing we are more likely to experience periods of boredom, anxiety and even despair. We may try to avoid these feelings with a frantic schedule but will increasingly seek to comfort – or numb – ourselves in addictions such as overeating, until we can experience very little pleasure without them. But this only makes the problem worse by further undermining our self-esteem. It causes us to find less and less pleasure in ourselves, and leaves us more likely to turn to addictions in an attempt to bring relief from our fundamental dislike of ourselves.

This vicious circle is most noticeable when we are alone, and low self-esteem often shows up as distress when alone with oneself. With nobody to distract us or to assure us of our worth, we are exposed to our own dissatisfaction with ourselves. Most overeaters eat addictively most often when they are alone. They don't want others to see how much they eat anyway, because other people's approval is always more important than their own.

This is the tragedy of low self-esteem: believing you're not valuable enough to stop overeating yourself into disease, premature ageing and untimely death. If you find you cannot care enough about yourself to start to do things differently, at least you can 'fake it till you make it'. Pretend to honour yourself more, act accordingly, and the higher self-esteem will follow.

Acting accordingly means using Times, Plans and the Outline to strengthen the 'six pillars' of your self-esteem:

- You live more consciously by becoming aware of your addictive thinking: your desire to eat food you don't need and the ways in which you try to justify satisfying that desire.

- You gain self-acceptance as you accept the fact that as someone who is addicted you will continue to experience an addictive desire. Instead of resigning yourself to a life of uncontrollable overeating, you choose to accept your addictive desire when you feel it.

- You gain self-responsibility by reminding yourself that it's your choice whether or not to satisfy your addictive desire: you always have the freedom to eat anything you want, as much as you want. You take responsibility for your health when you make the healthiest possible choices, both in terms of quality and quantity.

- You have integrity when you keep your word to yourself by sticking to your Times and Plans, and when you spot the lies you tell yourself about what and how much you eat.

- You practise self-assertion when you say 'No, thanks' to others, both in refusing food when it's appropriate and in refusing to prioritise looking a certain way in order to gain their approval.

- You live purposefully by consciously declaring your physical and emotional health as your primary goal, and set out, choice by choice, to achieve that goal.

New Signs of Success

Perhaps all this seems like far too much to remember. All you need to *do* is to switch your focus from how much you weigh to whether or not you are in control of your addictive eating. As with any goal, it's important to be able to check on how you're doing as you go along. Instead of seeing success in terms of getting into smaller-size clothes, start to create a new standard of success:

Choosing Times and Plans, and keeping to them. This brings you a real sense of control.

A more positive response to addictive hunger. This is a sign you have shifted your motivation from weight to taking control. When weight is all you care about, there's no reason to accept the uncomfortable feeling of an unsatisfied addictive desire; you could avoid it and get the same result. When control of addiction is your aim, it makes perfect sense because this is exactly where your success lies.

A more positive response to natural hunger. As a result you have more energy and feel lighter in your body instead of heavy from overeating. This is a sign you have worked through your addictive thinking, and taken more responsibility for your choices.

Better health and vitality. This comes from eating less and making healthier choices about what you do eat.

Eating more of your food earlier in the day and less in the evenings. Most addictive eating is done in the evening, which means you digest food when you are the least active, which is not good for your health. It's only when you have come to terms with your addictive desire to eat, which usually surfaces later in the day, that you can start to correct the balance.

Staying off the scales. This means you are developing your sense of self-worth based on *your* opinions of yourself, not on what other people think of you.

Keeping this process and any weight loss as private as possible. This means you are doing this more for yourself, because you like being in control of your eating. When you discover that you can cope with life's ups and downs without overeating, this will mean far more to you than anything anybody else can ever say.

In other words   **JUSTIN**

My relationship with food was a real mess. I was devoting a lot of time and energy to thinking about what I was going to eat while living in denial about how much I ate, and also the quality of my food. My weight gained steadily over the years, I felt lousy about the way I looked, and the food I was eating. My self-esteem plummeted, perpetuating the cycle.

Eating Less has enabled me to take control. It has encouraged me to take responsibility for my eating, and to recognise the consequences of the choices that I make. I've finally made the connection that if I eat a load of 'garbage', then I probably won't feel good about it, or myself.

I now feel lighter, have more energy, a pride in my new habits and hope for the future.

TAKING CONTROL

• What might you currently be doing in order to avoid feeling your addictive desire to eat? Smoking, shopping, keeping yourself extra busy? Make a plan to deal with this so that you can gain more acceptance of your addictive desire. Remember, this is how you make real, lasting changes in your relationship with food.

• Find out what diseases members of your family have suffered or died from. This will give you clues to your genetic inheritance, and therefore what you are likely to be susceptible to. Find out how diet affects these conditions. This will show you the foods which are especially dangerous for your health.

Remember, you will still have the choice to eat these foods. You will still experience a desire for them. And you will probably try to justify eating them.

This applies just as much if members of your family have died as a result of addiction – to smoking, alcohol or eating, for example. This indicates that you could have a genetic predisposition to become addicted, so the techniques and principles in this book will be even more valuable for you.

References

1. Whether you are a smoker or an ex-smoker, my book *How To Stop Smoking And Stay Stopped For Good* (Vermilion) will show you how to deal with your addictive desire to smoke.

2. This information on appetite suppressants was taken from an article which appeared in *Time* magazine on September 23, 1996. *The New England Journal of Medicine* (August 28, 1997) published an editorial on diet pills which included the following passages:
   'It has never been shown, and it is highly implausible, that appetite-suppressant drugs can maintain weight loss indefinitely. To date, studies of these drugs have demonstrated efficacy only for short-term weight loss. Their safety if taken over a period of many years is doubtful, since the risk of serious toxicity appears to increase with the duration of use.
   'The medical community should be skeptical of quick pharmacologic fixes for obesity and should continue to support the view that alterations in diet and physical activity – though difficult to implement and sustain – will always be central components of prevention and treatment.'

3. An excellent book on the difference between healthy and unhealthy guilt, and how to heal the latter, is *Guilt Is The Teacher, Love Is The Lesson* by Joan Borysenko (HarperCollins).

12 What's for Dinner?

How do you decide what to eat? Do you go for whatever seems most enjoyable to you? If so, how can you know whether or not your addictive desire is dictating what kind of food you choose? To take an extreme example of this, a person could eat very little in quantity, eat according to Times and Plans, and eat nothing but chocolate bars and crisps. By our definition this would still be addictive eating.

Remember from Chapter Five that addictive eating is defined as eating anything other than what it is your body needs to stay in good health. For the quantity of your food, use Times and Plans. Here we look at quality. Food of the highest quality is food that meets your nutritional needs, and the lowest is food that does nothing more than satisfy your addictive desire.

The more you meet your nutritional needs and the less you feed your addiction, the more control you have. Of course, you'll need to know what your nutritional needs are so you can tell when you're thinking about eating something you don't need. If you don't know the difference, you won't be able to identify your addictive desire so clearly.

How can we be sure what our nutritional needs are? As I've said, I have little confidence in a 'natural instinct' that tells me what I need or what I don't need to eat. I suspect that my addictive thinking has camouflaged any intuition I may have been born with. I'm not saying intuition doesn't exist, nor that it is lost forever. But, at least for now, I need to rely on the advice of others. If it were only up to me, I wouldn't know which foods were damaging my body until it was too late.

Fortunately, I do have this information, and so do you. We know that people get ill and even die prematurely as a direct result of eating too much of certain kinds of food and not enough of other kinds. It happens gradually, but it happens and it continues to happen to an enormous number of people. It is possible that some of the information we are given about nutrition at any one time is incorrect, but the most responsible approach – and therefore the one that rewards us with the highest self-esteem – is to eat according to our best evaluation of the advice that's currently available.

There is certainly controversy in the field of nutrition; no two experts agree on every detail of the best possible diet. But it is precisely this controversy that makes the overwhelming consensus of opinion on some things so compelling. When it comes to refined sugar, refined flour, salt and fat, there really is a great deal of agreement.

I've selected some passages from books and leaflets to give you an idea of what I'm talking about. As you read these extracts, remember that you choose what you eat; nobody is making you do anything against your will.

Too much dietary fat not only causes an increase in body weight because fats are so high in calories but it is also associated with an increase in blood fat levels, which lead to fatty deposits in the blood vessels, especially those supplying the heart.

(British Heart Foundation leaflet)

... excessive fat and sugar content contributes to the accumulation of wastes in the tissues which impair proper cellular nutrition and encourage the formation of a kind of sludge in the bloodstream that can impede good circulation.

(Kenton, *The New Ultrahealth*)

Saturated fats are found in animal protein sources and in whole-fat dairy products ... they tend to raise insulin levels by creating a condition known as insulin resistance.

(Sears, *The Zone*)

Throw out all oils other than olive oil ... get rid of any margarine, solid vegetable shortenings and products (such as cookies and crackers) made with them.

(Weil, *Eight Weeks to Optimum Health*)

High temperature makes the oil oxidise so that, instead of being good for you, it generates harmful 'free radicals' in the body. Frying is therefore best avoided as much as possible, as is any form of burning or browning fat.

(Holford, *The Optimum Nutrition Bible*)

The eating habits of the population also play a significant part in the development and prevention of stroke, as blood pressure is affected by obesity, alcohol consumption and sodium (salt) intake.

(Department of Health, *The Health Of The Nation*)

The average western diet contains far too much salt, which causes edema (water retention) and also tends to deprive your body's tissues of oxygen . . . Fresh vegetables and grains and pulses have plenty of sodium chloride in them – all your body will ever need.

(Kenton, *The New Ultrahealth*)

The best choices . . . are always products derived from whole grains, such as whole grain breads and cereals. More of their nutritional value is intact, and they contain more fibre.

(Greene and Winfrey, *Make The Connection*)

Too little dietary fibre slows down the digestive processes, resulting in bowel disorders and constipation.

(British Heart Foundation leaflet)

. . . if you do eat unfavourable carbohydrates – especially bread – always use the whole-grain versions.

(Sears, *The Zone*)

Reduce consumption of white sugar and sweets in general. Diets high in sugar are most likely to be deficient in protective factors. Reduce consumption of packaged and highly processed foods, which are similarly deficient.

(Weil, *Eight Weeks to Optimum Health*)

Too many processed foods, prepacked, precooked, junk food, fast food – whatever they are, they contain too much animal fat, salt, additives and too little fibre.

(Stoppard, *Woman To Woman*)

We consume volumes of foods with a high level of phosphorus, which impedes absorption of good nutrients. Examples of these foods are soft drinks of low or normal calorie types, processed foods, canned, packaged, pre-packed, convenience foods and ready-made sauces.

(Stewart, *No More PMS*)

In the process of refining sugar, every vestige of life and nutrient is stripped from it. All the fibre, vitamins, minerals, everything is virtually removed, leaving only a deadly remnant.

(Diamond, *Fit For Life*)

In the primitive societies of developing countries, where people live on a diet of mostly unrefined carbohydrates, little or no sugar and very little fat, our common illnesses, from varicose veins and coronary heart disease to diverticular disease, are virtually unknown. That is, until a typical western diet, including white bread, sugary foods and so on, arrives. Then these illnesses begin rapidly to appear.

(Kenton, *The New Ultrahealth*)

The chances are you are well aware of all this information, and have already made changes in your eating in view of the well-established, well-known health risks of certain foods. However, if you are overweight or if you already suffer from diet-related illness, this is a good indication that you haven't yet made enough changes. This is very common. The reason it's so common is that, on their own, all the advice and all the information are not enough – you still have addictive thinking to deal with!

This means you will experience your addictive desire – especially for refined sugar, refined flour, fats and salt. It is possible to eat healthy food in an addictive way (masses of apples, for example) but most people find their addictive desire is strongest for those foods with the most addictive qualities.

If I chose my food influenced *entirely* by my addictive desire, I'd only eat things like pizza, taramasalata, fried bread, sausages, cream pastries and chocolate-covered raisins – to name but a few. I wouldn't eat fruit or green vegetables at all.

I'm not alone, of course. Many of my clients tell me they don't like fruit and they don't really fancy green vegetables, especially not every day, especially not raw, especially not without creamy dressings, and especially not as the main part of their diet.

This is all part of the addiction. When you are accustomed to feeding your addictive desire, you won't find nearly as much gratification in food without fat, salt or refined sugar and flour. *An apple just won't satisfy as much as an apple pie with cream will.*

Most of the time you choose between your nutritional needs and your addictive pleasures. Or you settle for a compromise somewhere in between the two. A nod in the direction of nutrition is often used to justify feeding the addiction again. For example, you'll eat steamed fresh broccoli – but only if it's covered in a creamy sauce. You order a side salad to start with – just so you can kid yourself that your pizza lunch was a healthy one. You snack on fruit in the afternoon instead of something sugary – so you 'reward' yourself with biscuits later on.

As we saw in Chapter Five, your pleasurable responses to food are an aspect of your addiction. If your taste-buds always have the last word, you will continue to eat addictively because they are, at least in part, the expression of your addictive desire.

It could be that you've made healthy changes in your diet up to the point where they come into conflict with your addictive desire. You've made some concessions, but continue to justify overeating fats, salt, refined sugar and refined flour in some form. Not only do you not need these because they don't supply you with essential nutrients, but the chances are you eat them in quantities that are actually dangerous to your health. *You'd be much more healthy without them.*

A lot of processed, fatty and salty food is available. It's the most addictive, and we are likely to be more attracted to it than anything else.

A good rule of thumb is: if it's advertised, it's likely to be addictive. Advertising costs a great deal of money, which means someone expects to make a great deal of money as a result, and, as any drug dealer knows, addictive substances are by far the easiest things to sell. This is why there's refined sugar and flour, fat and/or salt in almost all commercially prepared foods, and this is why people keep eating them. There is no other reason. (1)

People who design and produce 'food' (i.e. things to eat) are guided by what will sell, not by a concern for your well-being. They care as little about your health as do the people in the tobacco industry.

What assists their marketing is that so many people assume they are healthy if they are not hospitalised or have no obvious signs of physical deterioration. This comes from having a standard of health based on more dramatic symptoms of illness. However, the fact that you don't have a serious illness doesn't mean you are in the best possible state of health. A serious illness is usually the final sign of a long-established state of ill health.

You can change your standard of health by paying attention to more subtle symptoms and finding out how the food you eat affects them. Do you ever feel tired after eating? Do you suffer from indigestion? Do you get headaches or PMS? Are you susceptible to infections? Do you have clogged sinuses? *These, and many more, are early warning signs that you are eating addictively much too often; too much in quantity and too little in quality.*

Take Care

I want to lodge a protest here and state that I don't particularly like the way things are. I know this sounds like my addiction talking, but I would prefer it if pepperoni pizza was as good for my health as cabbage. I'd rather eat egg mayonnaise sandwiches than salad for lunch, and I'd rather have crisps than pumpkin seeds for snacks.

Unfortunately, it doesn't matter what I want. My body simply isn't designed to work that way. It's like wanting to run my car on tap water: it doesn't matter how much I want it to or how much I complain about it – it just won't work!

Whenever I fight against reality, it's me who gets the bruises. The more I fight it, the more bruised I get. The bruises in my case were acid indigestion, loss of energy and a very real dent in my self-esteem that I only became aware of when I started to make changes. The more wisely I eat, the better I feel – physically, mentally and emotionally. That's just how it is. You don't have to take my word for it. Check it out for yourself.

You will need to take great care, though. The culture we live in tends to regard addictive food as normal, wholesome and even something to be highly prized. You will need to outwit not only the food industry, but also the slimming industry, possibly your family and friends and above all, your own addictive thinking:

☐ **Labels**   Read labels so that you know what you are eating. This doesn't necessarily mean standing in the supermarket studying every item before it goes into the trolley. You can read labels at home to learn how to make wiser choices the next time you shop. Be aware, though, that the labels are often designed to deceive you:

∗ When the contents are listed per serving, take into consideration how many servings you are really likely to be eating when you buy the item.

∗ Ingredients must be listed in order of amounts used in the product, with the largest ingredient first. But there are ways of dividing the contents into two listings – two different kinds of sugar, for example – so the total amount appears smaller.

∗ Salt content is not clearly labelled. Multiply sodium content by 2.5 to find the percentage of salt in a product.

∗ Be cautious of products labelled 'low fat'. All this means is there is less fat in this item than there would have been in a similar product. It's easy to use the 'low fat' label to justify eating more of it than is good for you.

∗ The term 'refined' in describing sugar and flour is very misleading. The 'refining' process was developed for commercial reasons in order to prolong the shelf life of food: these products have been 'killed' so they won't 'die' naturally in the shops. They have been stripped of nutrients. Far from being refined, they have been *destroyed*. (2)

☐ **Calories** Don't avoid foods solely because of their calorie content. They may provide you with important nutrients. Peanuts, for example, are high in iron and vitamin E – and they don't have to be coated in oil and salt! Beans and lentils are good sources of minerals, fibre and B vitamins. Calorie content alone isn't a complete guide to what's best to eat.

☐ **Anti-nutrients** Some foods have the effect of cancelling out other nutrients, so eating them is worse than eating 'empty calories'. Eating them actually contributes to a nutritional deficiency. This is very important, because many overeaters will choose something 'sensible' such as a salad, and follow it with a 'treat', such as a chocolate bar, cake or pastry. As far as your health goes, the 'treat' could be undoing the benefit of the salad.

Most manufactured foods contain anti-nutrients. Sugar, for example, provides no nutrition whatsoever, and depletes essential chromium and B vitamins. Most oils deplete vitamin E and block the body's ability to absorb the oils we need. (3)

☐ **Oils and ageing** There can be a big difference between our chronological age and our biological age. In other words, the number of years since we were born doesn't necessarily relate to the condition of our body. For example, one very famous overeater, Elvis Presley, was said to have the arteries of a man twice his age. In his forties when he died, he had overeaten so much, his body reflected a biological age of eighty.

The ageing process is accelerated by an increase in the production of unstable molecules in our bodies called free radicals. The main source of free radical damage in our food is from trans-fatty acids, that is, fats that have been chemically altered, found in cooking oils, margarines and all the products made with them. They are positively bad for you. That's why nutritionists are now recommending we only use small amounts of olive oil and/or butter, and fry seldom if at all.

Free-radical damage is counteracted by the antioxidant nutrients, found in fruits, vegetables, whole grains, nuts and seeds.

☐ **Fruits and vegetables** It is now widely accepted that the best thing you can do for your health is to eat a wide variety of fruits and vegetables every day. Many people find this difficult to do for many different reasons. Taking vitamin and mineral supplements will not compensate.

I double my consumption of fruit and vegetables by taking *Juice Plus*, which is made from whole food, and thus contains the enzymes, phytochemicals and fibre as well as the vitamins and minerals. (4)

☐ **Books** Many books on the market explain the links between food and specific health problems, and there are good books on nutrition in general. You may already own some. Most of my favourites are mentioned in this book.

Books on weight loss usually contain sound nutritional advice, but tend to reinforce improving your appearance as a priority. Even so, they provide many health-conscious ideas, such as ordering salad dressing on the side in a restaurant, using fresh lemon instead of salt, and stir-frying with flavoured vinegar or wine.

Increase Quality, Decrease Quantity

It's no coincidence that we tend to overeat those foods that are the most damaging to our health. As we saw in Chapter Ten, these foods trigger chemical events in our bodies which, although they are not good for our bodies, feel good to our minds.

Those natural and positive responses we get from eating are simply exaggerated by overeating (too much in quantity) and by commercial processing (too little in quality). So we get more enjoyment and satisfaction than is good for us, which makes eating such foods both a result and a cause of addictive eating.

To make matters worse, we tend to think we aren't really allowed to eat these foods, and this makes us want them more. We need to know we are free to do whatever we want, so if we don't take responsibility for our own choices, we rebel by eating the 'forbidden' foods.

There's no other reason for these products to exist. A kind of collective denial in our culture makes them seem acceptable, but apart from satisfying our addiction, all those products do is make us ill. Addiction is the only reason they're eaten, the only reason they're bought, and the only reason they're made in the first place.

This is an important point to grasp because making changes in what you eat could be as significant as – or even more significant than – making changes in how much you eat. Remember that you always have the choice either to satisfy or to accept your addictive desire for these foods. Remember that by accepting your desire you gain in health and vitality. *Remember that there is also great pleasure to be found in high self-esteem.*

You don't need to completely eliminate your addictive eating. Simply aim to do it less and less often. The more you gain an acceptance of your addictive desire, the easier this process will become.

When we eat 'as nature intended', both in terms of the quality and the quantity of our food, we will look, feel and be our best. Even though what nature intends may not always be clear, a sincere and consistent effort in that direction will bring us far more rewards in terms of health and self-esteem than deciding it's all too confusing to bother with. Many overeaters remain ignorant and confused about nutrition simply to continue to justify their addictive eating. (5)

Don't imagine that the decision to eat in a healthier way is made in a single moment. It's not. It's a decision that's made over and over and over again, every time you make a choice about food, every time you eat, every time you think about what to have for dinner.

You can take a break, though, when you go on a fast, and that's what we'll look at next.

In other words   **JUDITH**

After I had finished the Eating Less *course I bought and read two books on nutrition:* The Optimum Nutrition Bible *and* Eight Weeks to Optimum Health *and started to eat according to those recommendations. I began with cutting out the bad fats, sugar, salt, refined flour, booze, caffeine, tea and any additives I could spot. Also chocolate, biscuits, cakes, etc. I drank water, watered-down fruit juices and herbal teas, and ate grains, pulses, fruit, vegetables, lean meat (only once a week) and fish.*

I have introduced breakfast where none was before and settled down quite happily to three healthy meals a day which are satisfying and colourful. I've done a lot of research into organic foods and food products I had never heard of before, such as quinoa. That has been an interesting voyage of discovery which is not over yet.

It has been enjoyable and I expect it to continue to be so. I do not miss chocolate, although I do miss cappuccino and Diet Coke.

I don't believe I would ever have been able to make these changes without learning what you teach in the Eating Less *course. I am able to identify and understand my addictive thinking, and I am able to deal with it. This has provided me with the context for the changes I have made.*

TAKING CONTROL

• Broadly speaking, there are two distinct styles of addictive eating:

   1. eating a complete and balanced diet, and then more than you need, either in quantity or quality or both

   2. eating poor-quality food without any serious attempt to meet nutritional needs.

If you identify with the first style, use Times, Plans and the Outline to eat less of the food you don't need.

Addictive thinking is behind the second style, too. Use the techniques to make choices to accept your addictive desire for the 'convenience' (fried, refined and processed) foods. You may need to put some thought and effort into how to provide yourself with good food daily. Actively seek out the shops, recipes and restaurants that provide better-quality food.

• Notice whether the food you eat satisfies your nutritional needs or your addictive desire. Tell yourself the truth whenever you are about to eat food you don't need. You'll want to eat it, you'll be free to eat it, you'll try to justify eating it – and at least sometimes you will eat it. Just get into the habit of identifying it for what it is.

• If you switch from eating mostly highly processed to mostly natural foods you may go through a period of detoxification, when you may feel tired and unwell for a week or two. Don't make the mistake of thinking these foods aren't good for you! They will save your life. To learn more about detoxification, read Patrick Holford's book *Beat Stress and Fatigue* (Piatkus).

• What is it about the quality of what you eat that you like most? What is it that you most want to change about the quality of what you eat?

• Discover a new recipe and/or restaurant meal that you enjoy, making sure it's healthier in some way than what you normally eat.

References

1. It's often said that people eat commercially prepared 'junk' food because it's less expensive, but in terms of nutritional value, you are much better off with food closer to its natural state. As a general principle, the more stages of processing a product has gone through – milling, chopping, cooking, designing, packaging, marketing – all of which cost money, the less nutritional value you'll get for your money. Notice that those cultures in our world today which have the most overweight populations are also the most affluent.

    Eating quantities of cheap, processed foods to 'fill yourself up' is doing little more than satisfying your addictive desire. Feeding most addictions is an expensive business, and food addiction can be one of the most costly to maintain.

2.   'Flour, rice and sugar lose more than 77 per cent of their zinc, chromium and manganese in the refining process. Other essential nutrients, such as essential fats, will not be present in processed foods . . .'
     From *The Optimum Nutrition Bible* by Patrick Holford.
     Much of the most recent advice on nutrition warns us against eating wheat in any form, suggesting we reduce our consumption and even eliminate it entirely, at least for a while to see if our health improves. It is certainly eaten too much as it's found in most prepared foods, and of course bread, pasta, pies, quiches, biscuits, pastries and cakes.

3.   'Taking large amounts of unsaturated fatty acids without extra vitamin E will quickly use up the body's supply of the vitamin.'
     From *Free Radicals and Disease Prevention* by David Lin.
     'Refining and processing vegetable oils can change the nature of the polyunsaturated oil. [Margarine, for example] blocks the body's ability to use healthy polyunsaturated oils.'
     From *The Optimum Nutrition Bible* by Patrick Holford.

4.   *Juice Plus* is made from seventeen different kinds of fruits and vegetables. The water and sugar have been extracted so they can be taken as capsules with water. The product is not available in shops. Call the makers' head office on 01628 776 044 or send me a SAE for a fact sheet. My PO Box address is at the end of this book.

5.   'Eating in a healthy fashion doesn't have to be complicated. In general, just try to eat more fresh vegetables, fruits, cereals and legumes. Limit your consumption of red meats and cold cuts, substituting poultry without skin and fish as often as possible. Avoid fried and other fatty foods. And substitute low- or non-fat dairy products for their whole-milk counterparts.'
     From *Biomarkers: The Ten Keys to Prolong Vitality* by Drs Evans and Rosenberg (Simon & Schuster).
     Regarding two recent reports on nutrition, one from the World Cancer Research Fund and the other by the British Committee on the Medical Aspects of Food and Nutrition Policy:
     'Both reports emphasise the importance of increasing intake of fibre and of fruits and vegetables to five or more servings a day. They also both recommend a reduction in daily red and processed meat consumption.'
     The British Medical Journal (315, October 4, 1997).

13 Gym and Tonic

As we become more mindful about what goes into our bodies, we can also learn more about what needs to leave it. Poisonous substances enter our bodies every day. We can't prevent this, and to some extent it's not a problem because we continuously filter out toxins and eliminate them. Our bodies do this automatically, just as our hearts beat with no need for our intervention.

But we are often exposed to significant amounts of toxins from a wide range of sources: additives, preservatives and chemical residues in food and drink, exhaust fumes and other airborne pollution, 'recreational' drugs including alcohol and caffeine, prescription drugs and tobacco smoke.

Some people experience extreme symptoms, but a great many of us suffer from some level of toxic overload without even realising it. Symptoms can develop such as: headaches, memory loss, weakness, depression, drowsiness, watery eyes, itchy nose, joint stiffness and muscle aches. When we continue to expose ourselves to so much toxicity and do little to counteract it, our health will suffer sooner or later.

So what can we do about it? First of all, we can avoid toxic chemicals as much as possible in the first place. The closer food is to its natural state, the fewer additives and preservatives you consume. The more organic fruit, vegetables and grains you eat, the less chemical fertiliser and pesticide residue you consume. The less factory-farmed meat and chicken you eat, the fewer growth hormones, insecticides and antibiotics you consume.

You can also help to detoxify your body by exercising and by fasting.

Exercise

Exercise assists detoxification, and it also plays a part in taking control of addictive eating. Much of your motivation to stay in control will depend on how good you feel physically. Eliminating the nausea, bloating and lethargy caused by overeating may well provide you with a strong incentive to continue to make different choices. The fitter you are, the stronger this motivation becomes and the more likely you are to notice and respond to more subtle changes in energy.

Most importantly, though, exercise of any kind helps to detoxify your body by increasing the amount of oxygen circulating in every cell and in every organ. Moving the outside of your body gets everything moving on the inside, flowing as it's supposed to do: circulatory system, lymph system, digestive system and the rest. It literally makes your body younger because it counteracts all the ageing processes. It enhances energy levels and reduces stress. As for your mind, exercise is one of the best treatments for depression. (1)

However – as many people know only too well – the problem is that the vast majority of those who take up some form of exercise abandon it before long. Boredom is often given as the explanation. If you are one of those who start but then stop exercising, and if you think the reason for this is boredom, it may help you to consider a different explanation.

Consider: we do many things each day that don't offer challenging intellectual stimulation. Any daily routine can be boring, but we do them because we are motivated to do them. We are motivated because we gain in some way.

So too can any exercise routine become boring, but the reason it's abandoned isn't boredom, it's *resistance*. This resistance is the gravitational pull of inertia – the tendency of matter to remain at rest unless affected by an outside force – and it's experienced in direct proportion to the amount of effort required.

Resistance shows itself as an objection to the prospect of taking exercise, when you 'get too busy' or decide you'd rather watch TV. Resistance can also be translated into feeling too tired. Although this looks like the perfect excuse to sit down and rest, notice that when you go ahead and exercise anyway, your energy *increases* as a result.

You should always expect to encounter resistance. It's a big mistake to think that one day unbridled enthusiasm for exercise will suddenly appear on your doorstep. Here are some suggestions to get and keep you going:

☐ **Redefine** Just as the word 'dinner' could mean a hundred different things to a hundred different people, so can the word 'exercise'. Unfortunately, many people have an extremely narrow definition, which usually includes pain, exhaustion and scanty leotards.

Define exercise as moving your body, as distinct from being still. All you need to do is to simply – and slowly – increase the amount of exercise you do. If you are unfit, it can actually be dangerous to increase exercise too rapidly because it puts excessive strain on your body. Then you're much more likely to give up on it all together. Push yourself up to your limits, but never beyond them.

Anything – a half-hour walk on a Sunday afternoon or using stairs instead of a lift – is better than *nothing*. Just make sure the exercise suits your body and your fitness. Some form of exercise is usually possible, even for those with bad backs, those confined to a wheelchair and for the elderly.

☐ **Motivate** As with motivation to eat less, motivation to exercise is much more effective if you think of it as taking responsibility for your emotional and physical well-being, instead of purely as a way to change the shape or size of your body.

I am more likely to keep exercising regularly when I regard it as the way for me to release toxins, stress and negative feelings such as anger and frustration – all of which are quite literally stored in our bodies and pose a genuine threat to health. I stay motivated to exercise because I experience benefits immediately: I feel much more positive about everything, I have more energy, I sleep better, I don't get lower back pain, I feel more relaxed and my digestive system improves. I think more clearly and often find I come up with wonderful solutions to all kinds of problems while at the gym.

☐ **Vary**   Walking is said to be the best form of exercise because it has the lowest risk of injury and it gets your heart and your lungs working. You'll get the best results if you stride out and keep up a brisk pace for as long as you can, ending up slightly out of breath but not gasping for air. Toxins are stored in fat cells, and fat mostly gets burned off after you've done about twenty minutes of exercise, so walk for half an hour or more to get the benefit.

Find a form of exercise you enjoy. When you begin to feel fed up with it, do something else for a while. Some people enjoy the competition involved in sports, for others exercise is a chance to connect with the natural world of trees, birds and sky. Sometimes this is what exercise brings to my life, and sometimes I take my Walkman to the gym and look forward to listening to my favourite music. If I get bored, I find another tape to play.

For me, though, it isn't boredom, it's resistance, and nine times out of ten, as I pick up my gym bag and put on my trainers, I think to myself that I'd rather do something less energetic instead. I suppose there are people to whom exercise comes easily and naturally, but I am certainly not one of them. Once at the gym, though, I do enjoy myself and afterwards I'm always glad I didn't give in to my resistance.

Fasting

Even if you haven't the slightest intention of ever going on a fast, do read this section. Fasting is not an essential part of the Eating Less technique, but if you read on you may begin to see fasting in a new light, and there are some details about addictive eating you may find helpful.

Fasting can help you in two ways. It promotes health because it helps to detoxify the body and, if done correctly, it can help you to work through your addictive thinking.

If I mention to people that I fast, their reaction is often one of serious concern for my well-being. Let me assure you that

I am, like most of us in the Western world, a long, long way from starving. Anybody who overeats would stay alive for at least a month on stored body fat alone. Overeaters' health problems are caused by too much food, rather than too little.

It may be that anorexia and bulimia have given fasting a bad name. Fasting itself is not dangerous. Millions of people fast for either health or religious reasons with no detrimental effects at all. Fasting becomes a problem only when it's done for the wrong reason: an extreme attachment to weight loss. When someone starts to fast because they are desperate to lose weight, it certainly can become a very real problem. The problem isn't fasting. The problem is believing that your life – and your self-esteem, which can feel like the same thing – depends on looking good, and fasting to achieve that.

Fasting, if done correctly, has an entirely beneficial effect on your physical health. As the authors of *Fit For Life* say:

> We eat and live in such a way as to never allow the insides of our bodies to be cleansed sufficiently, and that is why 62 per cent of the population of this country is overweight. It is also a contributing factor to the fact that three out of four people in this country will develop some form of heart disease or cancer in their lifetime. The outside of the body is washed, but the inside, which is far more important, is not washed. I'm talking about some people going for decades, their entire lives, without ever doing what is necessary to wash out the toxic waste from inside their bodies.

There are very good reasons to go on a detoxification fast. However, for some people there may be even better reasons not to fast. Consider these, and decide what's right for you.

Good Reasons Not to Fast

☐ *It's not a good idea to fast* if you are desperate to lose weight or if you have a history of anorexia or bulimia. A detoxification fast could result in some weight loss, but fasting isn't the best way to lose weight anyway, because, as you probably know, your metabolism slows down when you don't eat for long periods of time.

☐ *It's not a good idea to fast* if you have a tendency to overeat either before or after a fast. As we discussed in Chapter Six, this is a rebellious reaction to the denial of choice. You'd be better off spending more time with Chapter Six, especially the exercises at the end, before you start to fast. Get used to reminding yourself that you always have choices. Then take a few short fasts to see how you react.

☐ *It's not a good idea to fast* if you go on a fast as a way to take control of your overeating. Don't fast to feel better about yourself, if you do a lot of addictive eating, and start to feel disgusted with yourself. This creates an 'all or nothing' attitude towards food. You are either overeating or fasting. Each state merely reinforces the other one.

People who spend most of their time either fasting or overeating aren't spending much of their time practising control, especially facing that strong addictive desire which gets triggered by eating. The best way to take control of your eating is by setting Times, making Plans and using the Outline.

☐ *It's not a good idea to fast* if you are not in the best of health, if you're coming down with an illness or recovering from one, or if you suffer from a condition such as diabetes or hypoglycemia. Get your doctor's advice if you have any concerns about the effect fasting may have on your health.

☐ *It's not a good idea to fast* if you don't normally eat a high-quality diet at other times. If you usually eat processed, poor-quality food, and then you fast, it's very likely you won't provide your body with the nourishment it needs. You will probably also experience unpleasant physical withdrawal symptoms, which are symptoms of detoxification. This is the point of the exercise, but if you end up with severe headaches and dizziness you may not want to fast ever again. When you first improve the quality of your diet, these symptoms won't appear when you fast.

How to Fast Non-addictively

There are many ways to fast. A fast can be as short as a night's sleep (that's why we call it breakfast!) or last many days. You can fast by eating just one kind of food – usually recommended are fruits such as apples or grapes – or you can just drink liquids and eat no solid food at all.

Most detoxification plans include fruit, sometimes a vegan diet, and usually cover a week or more, and it may be that it suits you to take the time once or twice a year to do a longer detox. However, if this seems a bit too long for you it could put you off the idea completely. Personally, I find that a discipline of fasting for twenty-four hours once a week is very beneficial both to my physical health and my addictive thinking.

I fast either by drinking liquids only, or sometimes by eating fresh fruit only, for twenty-four hours, from one evening to the next, from 6 pm to 6 pm the following day, for example. I choose different days of the week depending on any social plans I may have. I don't do this continuously, but I return to it as a weekly practice because I enjoy it and gain great benefits from it.

The best reasons to fast are to remove toxins from your body and to help you to gain control of your addiction. If it's not done correctly, it could reinforce your addiction by encouraging feelings of deprivation and negative reactions to addictive and natural hungers. If you do fast, it's important to do it in a way that deals positively and effectively with your addictive thinking, rather than reinforcing it.

Here are my suggestions:

• Determine what kind of fast you are going to go on and how long it will last before you begin. Set a Time just as you normally would, the Time being when you say you are going to end your fast. The addicted mind thrives on confusion, so it's important to set clear goals. It wouldn't be so good to decide to fast only after realising you happen to have not eaten for a rather long time. In the same way, it isn't a good idea to start a liquids-only fast and half-way through decide to eat fruit – unless you have a genuine concern for your health, such as feeling shaky.

• Set Times and Plans for the fruit if you think you may eat it addictively.

• Fruit is best eaten raw, as it contains all the enzymes which detoxify your system. Because they are rich in simple sugars, most fruit juices create excess insulin, so it may be better to avoid them. Eat whole fruit for the water-soluble fibre it contains, too.

• Drink water, bottled or filtered, as you normally would. About eight glasses a day is usually recommended.

• For a liquid fast, I take the amount of money I would have spent on food and splash out on these high-quality, high-nutrition liquid alternatives, available from most healthfood shops:

    organic vegetable juices and broth
    miso soup
    green drinks
    protein/carbohydrate drinks

It's very unlikely you'll feel weak or tired if you are drinking enough, but if you do, drink one of these immediately.

• I don't set Times and Plans for these high-nutrition drinks, but by all means do so if you want to, so that you don't drink addictively, simply replacing addictive eating with drinks. A bad taste in your mouth is a sign the toxins are coming out, and you may want to use a mouthwash.

• Coffee, tea, alcohol and fizzy drinks are counter-productive because they contain toxins and because, in the absence of solid food they are likely to give you an acid stomach. Drink them very little, if at all.

• If you are new to fasting, try eight hours to begin with. Twenty-four hours once a week is probably the maximum you should attempt. Fasts can be relatively easy times, because while you are fasting you are not making such challenging eating choices.

• Fasting gives you a good opportunity to pay attention to your experiences of addictive and natural hungers, and to work on gaining an acceptance of them. It's best not to drink when you feel a strong addictive desire to eat. Instead, use the Outline and make a clear choice to accept it.

You will notice that your natural hunger comes and goes, and that it's possible to experience natural hunger without any addictive hunger. It's also possible to experience addictive hunger (your addictive desire to eat) without any natural hunger. And it's possible to experience both at the same time.

• During your fast, go about your business as you normally would for the day. I fast while living my life as usual, and it's very important to me to be able to do that. I find I have plenty of energy for a work-out at the gym, even towards the end of a twenty-four-hour fast. Fasting in this way helps you to lessen the grip of many justifications for overeating, because you experience for yourself how you can carry on with your life going for longer periods of time with no food at all.

• Fasting also provides you with an opportunity to work through any feelings of deprivation. In order to do this, keep reminding yourself that you always have choices, and keep making your choices in the present time, both before and during the fast.

You may notice yourself projecting into the future as soon as you begin a fast, thinking: 'Now I can't eat anything for the next twenty-four hours!' Aim to fast for twenty-four hours (or however long you've chosen) but realise you can only accomplish this by making choices in each moment as it comes.

You are likely to experience symptoms of deprivation if you don't train yourself to make all your choices in the here and now. Remind yourself that you cannot choose to eat or not to eat in the future. Choices only function in the present time – at the moment you make them. Otherwise, they cease to be genuine choices!

• Before you begin your fast, eat lightly, or at least no more than you normally would. Otherwise you are trying to avoid feeling your hunger – or, more likely, feeling deprived – for the duration of the fast. This usually comes from the fear: 'I won't be able to eat for a long time, so I'd better eat as much as I can now.' No one is making you do this. If you are fasting, it's your choice. If you are hungry, it's your choice. If you are not satisfying an addictive desire to eat, it's your choice.

A fast can be a positive experience. Staying in the present time and choosing to fast moment by moment makes all the difference. If you do this you will see that fasting can be an enjoyable thing to do, that it's very satisfying and even exhilarating. You will see for yourself how energised your body feels and this is an invaluable experience for you in breaking your addiction to food. The exhilaration results from the tremendous sense of accomplishment you get from taking on such a challenge.

In other words   KATIE

Fasting is the area of the book I felt most resistant to – I just didn't want it to be true. It made good sense, though, so eventually I decided to give it a go.

My first attempt was a twenty-four-hour fast from 7 pm on Friday to 7 pm on Saturday. I booked it in my diary several weeks before and it helped me to eat high-quality food and less quantity in the lead-up because I knew that the more 'poison' there was in my body the harder it was going to be. I also planned my last meal and first meal very carefully to reduce the risk of panic eating.

During the fast all I consumed was water and some organic vegetable juice (which I thought was disgusting!). I went to the supermarket, did a hard session of aerobics, went shopping in central London with a friend, had a lively afternoon visiting my family and then went to the cinema. The worst bit was the last four hours. I developed a headache and had an incredibly strong desire to eat.

Fasting has given me an extra tool I can use. When the voice of my addictive desire shouts: 'I'm hungry; you must feed me now,' I can reply: 'Don't be stupid, if I can go for twenty-four hours without eating, I can certainly make it for four.'

Does fasting have long-term benefits for my health? I don't know. Does it make me feel good about myself? Absolutely.

TAKING CONTROL

• If you don't already exercise at least four times a week, discover and try out a new form of exercise that you enjoy.

• Look for opportunities every day where you can walk instead of taking a car, bus, lift or escalator.

• If you are ready to take another step towards taking control and enhancing your health and vitality, set a date and a time for a fast. Plan exactly what you are going to be consuming over the fast, and make sure that it's available.

References

1. Among other authors, Leslie Kenton makes these points about exercise in many of her books. An article which appeared in *Vogue* in June 1996 quotes Dr Ann Walker, senior lecturer in human nutrition at Reading University and Dr Susan Jebb, obesity expert from the Dunn Clinical Nutrition Centre in Cambridge:
    ' "We are now so sedentary," said Ann Walker, "that we cannot eat sufficient food to gain the micronutrients we require without getting fatter." Dr Susan Jebb said, "The lack of physical activity is

one of the most important factors in obesity, heart disease and strokes." '

An enormous study of twelve thousand Finnish adults over five years concluded:

'Low levels of physical activity were identified as a more important risk factor for excess weight than any features of the habitual diet.'

European Journal of Clinical Nutrition (1991; 45, 419–30)

14 Eating for Life

Times, Plans and the Outline are tools for you to use, and just like any other tool their purpose is to make the job easier. After all, you might be able to get a nail into a piece of wood without a hammer, but if you have a hammer why would you bother to try?

Like any other tool, they don't do the job for you; they only work when you use them. And, like most tools, it may take you a while to get used to them, so at first they may feel awkward, requiring some effort and concentration.

'The job' in this case is *accepting your addictive desire to eat*. By using these tools you can make that acceptance real to you as a functioning part of your life, thereby transforming your relationship with food. Gradually it becomes a part of your thinking, it becomes something you own.

The addictive desire isn't going to go away. You can either satisfy it or accept it. (You can also avoid it, but only temporarily.) Accepting the desire isn't accomplished instantaneously. The Outline enables you to accept it by weighing up the choices open to you.

When you don't use the Outline – and it needs to be used deliberately and consciously – your addictive thinking takes over by default. This means you're likely to react as if you don't have a choice, you'll resent and resist the desire and forget your motivation to accept it.

Addiction creates 'selective memory', especially when you are feeling your addictive desire. This means you are likely to remember only the good things about satisfying it and forget the bad consequences – until later on, when the desire is satisfied and you remember and regret what you've done.

Your deliberate use of the Outline will counteract this selective memory.

The real challenge may be in spotting your addictive desire in the first place; Times and Plans make it much easier to see.

The Outline (See page 100)

Step 1 *'I have a desire to eat.'* First of all, you acknowledge that you have an addictive desire, and remind yourself that this is inevitable, simply because you have eaten addictively in the past.

Step 2 *'I have the freedom to eat.'* When you acknowledge the fact that you have a choice, you'll be able to make one. You understand that it's your choice to take control. Then, and only then, you are neither complying nor rebelling. You are taking responsibility.

Step 3 *'I choose to accept my addictive desire . . .'* This is the most important step. Remember, the only reason you did not have control in the past is that you were not willing to experience the uncomfortable feeling of an unsatisfied addictive desire to eat. By choosing to accept it, you turn it into a positive experience and gain control.

Step 4 *'. . . to gain the benefits of . . .'* You break free from an addiction by resolving the conflict it creates in you. You do this by choosing to feel your addictive desire because this is worthwhile to you, because of whatever it is that you get as a result of taking control of your overeating.

Write down these benefits. Your addicted mind will tend to forget them, especially those benefits other than losing weight.

In and Out of Control

The great majority of my clients are delighted when first introduced to the Eating Less technique. They set Times, make Plans and experience real benefits as a result. They feel in control of their eating, often for the first time in years. They have more energy, feel healthier and enjoy better self-esteem.

But sooner or later, their enthusiasm fades. They stop setting Times and eat beyond their Plans. They eat addictively more and more often, and then begin to wonder what went wrong.

Perhaps you have had a similar experience. Maybe you've already started to use these techniques, and although you find them helpful when you use them, you don't use them often enough, or you suspect that it's just a matter of time before you lose interest.

Relax. I never assume that anyone, including me, will use these techniques consistently each and every time they eat, every day for the rest of their lives. This assumption is not only unrealistic, but dangerous.

Taking control of addictive eating is a long-term process. There will be lots of ups and downs along the way. This is not meant to sound discouraging. If you don't acknowledge this, you are more likely to feel hopeless when you do lose control, so that you don't want to use the technique ever again. However, if you understand that it's inevitable that you'll lose control at some point, when you do, you will realise that all you need to do is to get back on track. Losing control is not the problem, it's believing that it should never happen.

While you use this technique, even if it's just for a limited period of time, you can't help but discover more about your addictive eating. If you only gain more insight into your addiction and what's running it, that's some progress. You are sure to achieve good results in the long term, unless you completely give up any involvement with this process. *One of the main reasons people give up is that they expect too much of themselves too soon.*

Taking control of addictive eating requires a steady process of growing awareness. Awareness of what food you need to stay healthy – and what you don't need. And awareness of your addictive thinking and the tricks it plays.

The first time you get back on track may well be the most significant, because this is when you establish for yourself

A PLAN FOR SUCCESS

BLOCKS TO SUCCESS

> You see success and failure
> in terms of weight
>
> *'Whenever I think about eating
> or not eating something, my
> weight, shape and size are all
> that really matter.'*

+

> You fear that permission to
> overeat will lead to overeating,
> so you think in terms of
> 'no choice' in order not to eat.
>
> *'I mustn't eat any more!
> I have to stop eating so much.'*

+

> Your addictive desire to eat
> is either repressed or feels
> overwhelming
>
> *'Eating less is easy for a
> while, but doesn't last. At
> some point I feel as if I've
> been possessed by something
> and I'm driven to overeat.'*

SOLUTIONS	RESULTS
• Focus on motivation that has to do with anything other than the weight, size and shape of your body.	Genuine, maintainable
• See Chapters Two, Three and Four	control
	over
	addictive
• Take responsibility by recognising that you always have the freedom to eat anything you want.	overeating:
	self-esteem,
• See Chapter Six	confidence,
	freedom,
	flexibility,
• Set Times and make Plans. Use the Outline as much as you can in order to develop a positive response to your addictive desire.	less body fat, more health,
• See Chapter Seven	vitality
	and energy

that you can regain control. As it happens again and again – and it will – you will simply learn to get back on track faster.

In time, you will find that you are able to increase the quality and decrease the quantity of what you eat during those times you are out of control. Gradually smooth out the roller-coaster ride of 'out of control' eating and 'in control' eating, so it's more like a bumpy road. When your 'out of control' eating is not very different from your 'in control' eating, you'll feel much more relaxed and confident about the whole business.

This confidence is something I hear about from clients, even a long time after they've done my course. *No one* follows the technique perfectly, but in general, they eat healthier food and less of it, and they feel better about themselves.

Here are some thoughts about staying in touch with this process in the long term. They may be especially helpful to read when you've 'lost it':

□ *Taking control is a process of taking more responsibility.*
Maybe things go well at first simply because you are 'being good' by complying with what you regard as a new set of rules and regulations – Times and Plans – just as you have complied with countless diets in the past. Although compliance looks like success, it will lead to rebellion sooner or later.

Don't worry about whether or not you're complying. If you are, all that will happen is that at some point you'll start to rebel – and that's when you really can start to make progress. At that point you'll begin to feel deprived or begin to eat more addictively, probably latching on to some compelling justification you've just discovered.

Your tendency not to take responsibility for your eating choices was there before you read this book: the Eating Less technique simply helps you to notice it. The technique then provides you with a way to work through it by reminding you of your free choices.

When you are not taking responsibility, you may eat a lot of 'forbidden' foods before you really believe you are free to eat them. You will undoubtedly be consuming far too much salt, fat and refined products than is healthy. Just work on eating these foods less often. To do this, simply choose to accept your desire for them more often. Always make your choices in the present.

□ *Taking control is about meeting different aspects of your addiction.*
Your more compelling feelings of desire, and your more convincing justifications for satisfying it, may surface long after starting to work with the technique. This is especially likely to happen if you've done a lot of dieting, when you've trained yourself to repress your addictive desire to eat for periods of time. You could get the impression that this is a lot easier than it actually is. It's only when things start to get more difficult that you can make real progress.

Here's an example that illustrates what I mean. I had been counselling Sarah for about six weeks when she explained to me that she was not at all in control of her eating, and couldn't possibly take control because her work schedule was far too demanding for her to spend time thinking about Times and Plans. Prior to this she had been using the technique for more than a month and was very pleased with the results. When we started to talk about it, she mentioned that her work schedule hadn't changed at all since we first met.

Sarah had simply come up against a new level of resistance, and had automatically selected the explanation for her overeating that sounded the most plausible.

A justification such as this is just like any other obstacle: if you don't see it, it's likely you'll trip over it. Get better at noticing your justifications and identifying them for what they are. Then, you can either use the justification to overeat or you can let it go. You can let it go in one of two ways:

(a) by seeing that the justification is false, as Sarah did, and not use it, or

(b) by seeing that it does contain some truth – for example, 'Yes, eating addictively does seem to comfort me' – but still choosing not to use it as a reason to overeat.

☐ *Taking control is about breaking specific patterns of addictive eating.*

Taking control of any addiction requires going through withdrawal. With most addictions, the behaviour is stopped completely and the addict is almost immediately faced with this most difficult phase of recovery. How they cope with that withdrawal – especially the mental side – determines their long-term success.

With overeating, of course, you don't give up food altogether. Instead, you go through a series of mini-withdrawals associated with particular foods and particular circumstances. Let's suppose you decide to stop eating chocolate after lunch every day. You make a Plan for lunch without the chocolate. When you finish lunch, you desire your familiar dessert and feel empty and a bit lost without it. You're in conflict about what choice to make. You struggle to identify your motivation while you re-evaluate your priorities. At this point, you are in withdrawal from food addiction.

This is how you change addictive behaviour. *Just like any other addict, you need to go through the experience of withdrawal in order to break free.* But with addictive eating, it doesn't happen all at once, it happens in bits and pieces.

In time, your addictive desire associated with that situation will fade, *provided you do not reinforce it by satisfying it with anything else, and provided you are genuinely choosing to accept it.* Like a fire, the desire burns itself out when it isn't fed. By the way, if you are very keen for it to fade, you're not fully accepting it.

You may also create *new* addictive patterns. You will see that whenever you do some addictive eating, your addictive desire will be reinforced, just as it would if you started smoking or taking any other addictive substance. If you started to eat ice cream every evening you would create an addictive desire for ice cream every evening. To break that pattern, you experience the feelings of desire and resolve your conflict about it.

With addictive eating, you only need to consistently break more old patterns of behaviour than you create new ones.

☐ *Taking control means discovering your limits to control.*
With most addictions, people are either completely out of
control of their addictive behaviour or completely abstinent.
Smokers either smoke all day, every day, or they don't smoke
at all. Many try to compromise, but find that the odd
cigarette here and there is impossible to maintain. You will
find this 'all or none' principle applies to overeating too, to
some extent, but only to some extent, and the extent to which
it does apply will be unique to you. You may not want to
stop eating addictively altogether.

You probably know what your limits to control actually
are. For example, you may know you are making an 'all or
none' decision when you open a bag of crisps or when you
buy a packet of Hobnobs. You may find that one bite before
your Time sends you completely out of control of your eating
for a week. Or a taste of sugar sends you off on a cookie
binge. Tell the truth to yourself about this when you are
making your choices. It will often be easier for you not to
take the first bite in the first place.

Taking a few bites before your Time or after your Plan
might not seem much of a problem at first, but it will erode
the effectiveness of the technique until you don't really have
a technique at all. You may need to experience this a few
times before you understand this.

As you work with this technique, you'll probably find that
your limits to control change. For example, you could find
that you've gained a degree of control that enables you to eat
only half a packet of crisps (assuming it's something you
want to do).

☐ *Taking control is a process of developing your motivation.*
Inevitably, you'll go through periods of time when your weight
matters less to you and other times when it matters more.
When your weight becomes more significant to you – and this
could be either because you haven't lost any or because you
have – you may react by eating more. If you experience big
variations in both the quality and quantity of what you eat – if
you are bingeing on junk food one day, nibbling on celery the
next – this is usually because weight loss is a primary goal.

It may take a while to put the goal of weight loss into a different perspective, so that it's not your *only* motivation. To begin with you may find it difficult to remember any reason other than weight to accept your feelings of desire, because your motivation may not be as strong and effective as it could be. A preoccupation with appearance will blind you to the more private and personal rewards of taking control.

While you are out of control, though, one thing you can discover is that being in control of your eating has greater value to you than just losing weight. You may need to be out of control a lot before you can really appreciate this. Keep observing how the quality of your life has improved in any way that doesn't involve your weight. Find any motivation that has to do with your health and self-esteem. (1)

☐ *Taking control changes your definition of 'hitting bottom'.*
Many alcoholics go through an experience which becomes a turning point, a time when they say: 'Enough is enough!' and begin to sober up. Perhaps a career was destroyed, a relationship ended or their life was in danger because of their drinking. The cost of the addiction had simply become too great. The alcoholic starts to believe that there must be a better way to live, that satisfying their addictive desire just isn't worth it any more.

This turning point is called 'hitting bottom', and it's often regarded as an essential part of successful recovery. Overeating, of course, doesn't always lead to quite such dramatic events as alcoholism does, but the same principle applies.

Every overeater will have a different personal definition of 'hitting bottom', but it's usually to do with weight. Your idea of it may be when you can't fit into a particular outfit, or when the scales reach a number you regard as significant. It's also possible that you have never hit your own 'bottom' and have no clear idea what it might be.

Remember: *you* are the one who decides when you will say: 'Enough is enough!' You are the one who determines what 'hitting bottom' for you actually is – and even whether you'll have one in the first place. Will it be your first heart attack? Or when you are diagnosed as diabetic? Or what?

My suggestion is to change your standards. Then, whenever you start to overeat, you can get back in control faster by refusing to put up with the consequences. Raise your standards, especially in any area other than your appearance. Remind yourself that your eating matters, that the quality of your life matters and that you matter. When I've eaten addictively, my energy and my self-esteem drop, long before I put on any noticeable amount of weight. Observe this for yourself, make it matter to you, and there's your motivation to get back on track faster.

☐ *Taking control is a natural process of ups and downs.*
Inevitably, there will be times when you have unexpected insights and breakthroughs, when you find you are able to make changes in your eating you never thought possible. It's also likely that times like these will be followed by periods when nothing seems to change at all. This too is to be expected, and there's nothing wrong with it. It's only a problem if you take it as evidence that the technique is useless or that you are incapable of using it.

Be patient. Staying at one level could mean you are ready to move on to the next. Perhaps you made some changes and then settled for an eating style which, although it is an improvement, is still compromise. You know that you're settling for something that's second rate, and that there's plenty of room for improvement. What is your next challenge?

Tolerating Imperfection

It will help a great deal to give up any ideas you have of perfect success. No one can stay perfectly in control of addictive eating. For one thing, there is no such thing as a perfect definition of addictive eating, and there never will be. You can only say whether or not you eat addictively in terms of degree: either 'a great deal' or 'not very much' or somewhere in between. Taking control of overeating is, by its very nature, an imperfect process.

Aspiring to perfection will get in your way. If you think perfection is a reasonable goal, no matter what you accomplish, you will focus on the one thing 'wrong'. Then it's all cancelled out. It's all meaningless.

Perfectionism may attract you because you think it will bring you security, that if you use the technique perfectly, you'll be sure to stay in control. The truth is that you could follow the Eating Less techniques to the letter for any given period of time, and then start to do a lot of overeating, completely out of control. Why? *Because it's not perfection that leads you to succeed in the long term; it's gaining an acceptance of your addictive desire to eat.* When you have achieved this to a significant extent, even when you do eat addictively, you will regain control by accepting your desire.

Think of accepting your addictive desire to eat as the payment you make in order to be in control. Do you prefer to be in control of your overeating? Then this is what it costs. It costs you moments of discomfort. If you make this payment, control of your addictive eating is yours to enjoy. If you don't make the payment, you lose it. The benefits are yours, not anyone else's, and so are the moments of discomfort while you feel your addictive desire.

The good news is that even if you are not perfect, you can always make progress. Half-way through a binge, if you can see the value of stopping right there and if you then make a choice to accept your desire to eat, that's *something*.

You will lose control, but all you need to do is get up one more time than you fall down. You will make mistakes. Simply notice them, forgive yourself, and learn from them.

This requires courage, because you are trying to do something that is extremely important to you, so any amount of failure will cause you to suffer. The 'safe' solution is not to try in the first place, or not to try too hard – but then nothing will change.

I've often found that it's precisely those times when I've felt the most hopeless that I am closest to a real breakthrough. The solution is right there in the problem, and all it usually takes is one or two very simple things to turn it around. Set yourself a Time, and then make present-time choices either to satisfy and reinforce your addictive desire to eat or to accept these addictive thoughts and feelings in order to gain the benefits you want.

When I'm in control of my eating I feel on top of the world, like there's nothing I can't do. All I need to do is pay the appropriate fee: an uncomfortable feeling of addictive desire. No, it's not easy and it's not magic – *but it works!*

In other words   HELEN

Really feeling my addictive desire to eat – that awful, tense longing and excitement – is very uncomfortable, but somehow it makes me feel more whole, as if I have regained a part of myself which I have been drowning in food, or diets, for years.

I'm finding your warning to tolerate imperfection very helpful. I'm really dismayed at the thought that I may go out of control again, but have to recognise the wisdom of it!

TAKING CONTROL

• Set a Time if you don't already have one. 'I'll start again tomorrow' is just another way to justify addictive eating in the present time. If you don't set a Time now, you're even less likely to do it tomorrow.

• Keep this book around you and read it again from time to time, perhaps just dipping in to a few pages or chapters. As you think more about these concepts, and especially when you use the technique a bit, coming back to the book will enable you to own it more and make it more meaningful.

References

1. Improvements to your general health as a result of improved nutrition will take time. Dr Michael Colgan provides some interesting details about this in his book 'Optimum Sports Nutrition':

    'The business of nutrition is to build a better body. That has to wait on Nature to turn over body cells. A blood cell lasts 60–120 days. In 3–4 months your whole blood supply is completely replaced. In 6 months almost all the proteins in your body die and are replaced, even the DNA of your genes. In a year all your bones and even the enamel of your teeth is replaced, constructed entirely out of the nutrients that you eat.

'This time course is well illustrated by the course of deficiency diseases. If I remove all the vitamin C from your diet, within 4 weeks blood vitamin C will drop to zero. But you will see no symptoms of disease at 4 weeks. You have to wait until enough of the healthy cells have been replaced by unhealthy cells. It is another 12 weeks before symptoms of scurvy start to ravage your body.

'So when you implement an optimum nutrition program, don't expect rapid results. In one of our studies at the Colgan Institute, runners were supplemented to try to improve their haemoglobin, hematocrit and red blood cell count. But after one month of supplementation, there was no improvement at all. After 6 months, all three indices were significantly increased.'

Index

Acknowledgements

I am very grateful to everyone who read drafts of the manuscript and gave me their comments, especially Melissa Nathan and Nina Planck.

I want to thank all my clients who have taught me so much, especially those who wrote about their experiences for the ends of the chapters.

And I would like to thank five people in particular who deserve special mention as important sources for the material in this book: Dr Nathaniel Branden, Dr K. Bradford Brown, Dr Mitra Ray, W. Roy Whitten and Joe Zeitchick.

Further Help

Gillian Riley is a counsellor and seminar leader who has been helping people to take control of smoking and overeating addictions since 1982. A former smoker and overeater, she brings to her work an understanding of the process of addiction gained through counselling others and through dealing with her own addictive behaviour.

Her book, *How To Stop Smoking And Stay Stopped For Good*, published by Vermilion, is available in most bookshops.

For information on Eating Less courses, send a stamped, self-addressed envelope to:

Gillian Riley
P. O. Box 2484
London N6 5UX

Eating Less Web Site
www.eatingless.com